why not develo[...]
which thrive on highly
acitic soils

private drillings of
wells regulated by
laws

GEOLOGY

About the Author

Richard M. Pearl is Professor of Geology at Colorado College, where he has been a member of the faculty since 1946. He is a graduate of the University of Colorado and Harvard University. Professor Pearl is a Fellow of the American Association for the Advancement of Science, the Meteoritical Society, and the Gemmological Association of Great Britain, and has received special recognition for his research and publications from scientific organizations in twelve countries. He is the author of twenty-two books on geology, minerals, and gems, including *Rocks and Minerals* in the Barnes and Noble Everyday Handbook Series, *Guide to Geologic Literature,* and *How to Know the Minerals and Rocks.* He is editor-in-chief of *Earth Science.*

College Outline Series

GEOLOGY

THIRD (REVISED) EDITION

Richard M. Pearl
Professor of Geology
Colorado College

BARNES & NOBLE, INC.   •   NEW YORK

PUBLISHERS   •   BOOKSELLERS   •   SINCE 1873

This is an original Outline (Number 13) in the original College Outline Series. It was written by a distinguished educator, carefully edited, and manufactured in the United States of America in keeping with the high standards of publishing.

Dedicated to
DR. PHILIP G. WORCESTER
Professor of Geology, Emeritus
University of Colorado

Preface

This book covers the introductory course in general geology, which is usually divided into one semester each of physical geology and historical geology, and the organization of topics follows the usual one for college courses. It may thus be used as a supplement to any of the standard geology texts listed in the Tabulated Bibliography.

A comprehensive survey and summary such as this book will help the beginning student to organize his studying and to obtain a different approach to the material covered in the regular textbooks. The advanced student should find it useful in reviewing the whole field for comprehensive examinations. It should also be valuable as a syllabus for classroom lectures, for adult study groups, and for individual programs of learning.

The author wishes to express appreciation to Dr. Samuel Smith, Editor of Barnes and Noble, and to Miss Nancy Cone and Mrs. Françoise Bartlett of the editoral staff for their assistance in the preparation of this Outline. He is also grateful to Professor Ralph J. Holmes of Columbia University for reading the manuscript and offering numerous helpful suggestions. Assistance in this revision has been received from Richard G. Beidleman, of Colorado College. Credit is given for the generous permission to use illustrations on pages where they appear.

In the revised third edition, Chapters 1 and 24 have been altered, and other changes have been made throughout the remainder of the book.

RICHARD M. PEARL

Table of Contents

Part II: Historical Geology

How to Study Geology

The principles of geology are best learned by studying a well-organized textbook and at the same time participating in laboratory work and field work to become familiar with the features shown by the earth itself.

The original school of geology is the field. Knowledge now found in books had to be acquired in the first instance by the direct observation of nature, in laboratory and field alike, and is useful only as a means of enabling us to take up the subject where others have left off, not as a substitute for further observation and reasoning. If your study of geology has not included laboratory work or field trips, be sure to inquire where examples of the features you are studying are located and make every effort to see and understand as many of them as you can. Visits to museums and other collections will make it possible for you to identify and interpret the rocks, minerals, and fossils you read about.

AIDS TO READING

Both physical and historical geology are best learned by emphasizing the basic principles involved, and so these subjects should be studied in their logical sequence. The history of the earth cannot be understood until the materials that compose it (minerals and rocks) and the processes that operate upon them have been learned.

Special attention should be given to the illustrations in geology texts. Visual aids such as photographs, diagrams, charts, and maps may teach you more than an equal amount of verbal description. Moreover, you may often find it necessary in examinations to reproduce parts of drawings and tables and to interpret selected illustrations. Incidentally, be sure always to read the captions under illustrations as carefully as the text. Try to correlate the information presented in different forms, such as a map and accompanying cross section. Formulas and equations should be understood, not merely memorized. The same is true of definitions.*

LABORATORY AND FIELD WORK

Laboratory work should be done as independently as possible, even when maps and other equipment or specimens must be shared. Each step of the work should be completed and the results carefully noted in order to insure thorough understanding of facts and principles. Field trips provide the best conditions for learning the subject matter of geology. If used for this purpose, they can still be just as enjoyable as any carefree outings.

REVIEWING

The most effective methods of reviewing vary with individuals. Some do best by means of visualizing; others find listening and oral expression most helpful. It is generally best to use a variety of approaches in order to take advantage of all possible means of learning. Make sure to read and reread each discussion, analyze it, pronounce and write down the technical terms, and formulate the definitions in your own words.

Reviewing Physical Geology. In reviewing a chapter of any textbook, you should construct and follow a definite plan. You will find it useful to make up a test for the chapter, covering the fundamental principles and the definitions of terms. Terms of comparable nature should be learned in groups, so that each term recalls to mind the others that belong with it. Thus, all the terms that refer to wind erosion will appear together in your review notes and therefore in your memory. Lists of terms should also be built up by opposites, so that wind erosion and wind deposition will stand opposite each other. Terms that pertain to residual features and transportational processes should be added to those of erosion and deposition. Landforms are conveniently considered on the basis of their structure (such as folded mountains) and their stage of development (young, mature, old). These lists provide a framework upon which you can attach de-

* Recommended for its many simple, practical suggestions, is *Best Methods of Study* by Smith, Shores, and Brittain (a companion book in the College Outline Series), which includes chapters on reading, writing, note-taking, and examinations.

scriptive matter. An example of each geologic process and feature, like those given in this book, often helps the student to recall the principle more easily than would a definition.

Reviewing Historical Geology. Basic principles, rather than mere descriptions, should be stressed here also. Geologic history should be thought of as cyclical in virtually every aspect. The recurrence of events—climatic changes, sea invasions, mountain uplifts—is more significant than any separate event, and the individual events can be fitted into the framework of time. Therefore, memorize the geologic time chart on p. 191 immediately and use it on every occasion. Note, also, that given geologic conditions such as episodes of glaciation, mountain-making, and large-scale deposition of minerals by evaporation, are often world-wide in scope. Associate the climate, topography, and main kinds of life of each geologic era in a single picture sufficiently simple and clear to give you the feeling of having seen it yourself, and you will then be able to recall it quickly. Formation names are hard to remember unless associated with something of interest, such as an important mineral product or noteworthy scenic feature for each formation. You may find it very worth while to make a chart of the earth's history as you review each chapter. Useful headings include: time unit, duration, distribution of land and sea, sedimentation, vulcanism, mountain-building, mineral resources, climate, plants, animals.

TABULATED BIBLIOGRAPHY OF STANDARD TEXTBOOKS

This *College Outline* is keyed to standard textbooks in two ways.

1. If you are studying one of the following textbooks, consult the cross references here listed to find which pages of the *Outline* summarize the appropriate chapter of your text. (Roman numerals refer to the textbook chapters, Arabic figures to the corresponding *Outline* pages.)

2. If you are using the *Outline* as your basis for study and need a fuller treatment of a topic, consult the pages of any of the standard textbooks as indicated in the Quick Reference Table.

Bates and Sweet, *Geology: An Introduction,* 1966, Heath.

I (1-9); II (13-23); III (183-192); IV (26-28, 80-84); V (95-100); VI (101-102); VIII (84-90); IX (175-182); X (183-187); XI (103-118); XII (127-137); XIII (119-126); XIV (45, 48-51); XV (90-94); XVI (45-47); XVIII (194-201); XX-XXII (202-208, 213-216, 220-225); XXIII (170-179); XXIV (200-201); XXV-XXVI (209-212); XXVII (216-219); XXVIII (229-235).

Branson, Tarr, and Keller, *Introduction to Geology,* 3rd ed., 1952, McGraw-Hill.

I (1-8); II (63-68); III (26-40, 80-84); IV (95-100); V (16); VI (103-117); VII (119-126); VIII (22, 145-152); IX (84-90); X (90-94); XI (127-137); XII (154-157); XIII (42-51); XIV (52-62); XVI (13, 165-167); XVII (194-200); XVIII-XXI (202-212); XXII-XXV (213-219); XXVI (220-227); XXVII (227-236).

Dunbar, *Historical Geology,* 2nd ed., 1960, Wiley.

II (188-190); III (175-188); IV (13, 165-167); V (170-175); VI (194-200); VII-XIII (202-212); XIV-XVI (213-219); XVII-XX (220-236).

Eardley, *General College Geology,* 1965, Harper & Row.

I (63-77); II (84-90); III (42-51); IV (26-32, 80-84); V (32-38); VI (90-94); VII (95-100); VIII (103-118); IX (119-126); X (145-153); XI (154-157); XII (127-137); XIII (20-25, 52-62); XIV (175-182); XV (183-193); XVI (194-201); XVII (202-208, 213-216, 220-225); XVIII (209-212); XIX (216-219); XX (229-234); XXI (225-229); XXII (234-235); XXIV (145-153).

Emmons, Allison, Stauffer, and Thiel, *Geology, Principles and Processes,* 5th ed., 1960, McGraw-Hill.

I (1-8); II (13-18); III (188-190); IV (16-17); V (63-77); VI (26-40); VII (80-84); VIII (95-100); IX (84-90); X (101-102); XI (103-117); XII (127-137); XIII (22, 145-152); XIV (119-126); XV (154-157); XVI (138-144); XVII (42-51); XVIII (90-94); XIX (52-62).

Garrels, *A Textbook of Geology,* 1951, Harper.

I (13-18); IV (52-62); V (22, 145-152); VI (154-157); VII (127-137); VIII (119-126); IX (84-90); XI (80-84); XII (90-95); XV (188-190); XVI (52-62); XIX (13, 165-167); XXI (175-179); XXII (194-236); XXIII, XXIV (170-182).

Gilluly, Waters, and Woodford, *Principles of Geology,* 1959, Freeman.

I (1-8); II (63-77); III (78-94); IV (95-100); VI (158-161); VII (183-193); VIII, IX (52-62); XI (101-102); XII (103-117); XIII (127-137); XIV (119-126); XV (154-157); XVI (22, 145-152); XVII (84-90); XVIII (26-40, 90-94); XIX (52-62); XX (42-51); XXI (74-76).

Holmes, *Principles of Physical Geology,* 2nd ed., 1965, Ronald.

I (1-13); II, III (14-27); IV (63-77); V (80-84); VI (84-90); VII (183-193); VIII (90-94); IX (42-51); XI (26-31); XII (32-38); XIII (188-192); XIV (95-100); XV (119-126); XVI (76-77); XVII-XIX (103-118); XX (127-137); XXI (225-229); XXII (154-157); XXIII-XXIV (145-153); XXV-XXVI (20-25, 52-62).

Holmes, *Introduction to College Geology,* 2nd ed., 1962, Macmillan.

I (1-8); II (13-18); III (63-77); IV (80-84); V (84-90); VI, VII (194-200); VIII-XI (202-212); XII-XIV (213-219); XV, XVI (220-225); XVII, XVIII (225-235); XIX (149-152); XX (52-62); XXI (103-117); XXII (119-126); XXIII (154-157) XXIV (76-77).

Kummel, *History of the Earth,* 1961, Freeman.

I (165-169, 183-193); II (170-181); III (84-90); IV (194-200); V, VI, VII (202-212); VIII, IX, X, XI (213-219); XII, XIII, XIV, XV (220-235).

Leet and Judson, *Physical Geology*, 3rd ed., 1965, Prentice-Hall.

I (1-8); III (13-15); IV (63-74); V (26-40); VI (80-84); VII (95-100); VIII (84-90); IX (185-192); X (101-102); XI (103-117); XII (119-126); XJII (127-137); XIV (154-157); XV (22, 145-152); XVI, XVII (42-51); XVIII (90-94); XIX (52-62); XX (16, 20-25); XXI (47); XXII (74-77).

Longwell and Flint, *Introduction to Physical Geology*, 2nd ed., 1962, Wiley.

I (1-8); II (13-25); III (63-80); IV (188-193); V (6-8, 158-161, 183-188); VI (26-40, 80-84); VII (95-100); VIII (101-102); IX (103-106); X (107-117); XI (119-126); XII (138-144); XIII (127-137); XIV (154-157); XV (145-149); XVI (149-152); XVII (84-90); XVIII (42-51); XIX (90-93); XX (20-25, 52-62); XXI (42-51); XXII (2-3, 7-8).

Longwell, Knopf, and Flint, *Outlines of Physical Geology*, 1941, Wiley.

I (1-8); II (63-77, 78-94); III (95-100); IV, V (103-117); VI (119-126); VII (138-144); VIII (127-137); IX (154-157); X (22, 145-152); XI (84-90); XII (26-40); XIII (42-51, 90-94); XIV (52-62); XVI (63-77).

Longwell, Knopf, and Flint, *Physical Geology*, 1948, Wiley.

I (1-8); III (95-100); IV (101-102); V, VI (103-117); VII (119-126); VIII (138-144); IX (127-137); X (154-157); XI (22, 145-152); XII (84-90); XIII (80-84); XIV (26-40); XVI (52-62); XVII (90-94); XIX (42-51); XXI (63-77).

Moore, *Introduction to Historical Geology*, 2nd ed., 1958, McGraw-Hill.

II (170-182); III (13, 165-167); IV (194-200); V-XII (202-212); XIII-XVI (213-219); XVII-XXI (220-236).

Putnam, *Geology*, 1964, Oxford.

I (13-19); II (63-77); III (26-38); IV (84-90); V (90-94); VI (42-51); VII (76-77); VIII (119-126); IX (20-25, 52-62); X (95-100); XI (103-118); XII (154-157); XIII (127-137); XIV (145-153); XV (45-47); XVI (170-182, 200-201, 209-212, 216-219, 229-235).

Spencer, *Basic Concepts of Historical Geology*, 1962, Crowell.

I (188-192); II (183-188); III, IV (4-5, 192-193); V, VI (165-

169); VII (194-200); VIII, IX, X (170-181); XI (16, 146); XII-XVII (202-212); XVIII-XX (213-219); XXI-XXIII (220-235); XXIV, XXV (171-175); XXVI (210-212); XXVII (212, 217, 232); XXVIII (229, 232).

Spencer, *Basic Concepts of Physical Geology,* 1962, Crowell.

I (1–8); II (13–18); III, IV (1–8, 76–77); V (18); VI (63–76); VII (26-40); VIII (80-84); IX (84-90); X (16-17, 21-23, 45-47); XI (20, 52-62); XII (17, 22); XIII (18); XIV (95-100); XV (101-102); XVI (103-117); XVII (127-137); XVIII (119-126); XIX (154-157); XX (115, 124, 131-136); XXI (147-152); XXII (145-147); XXIII (90-93); XXIV (42-51).

Stokes, *Essentials of Earth History,* 2nd ed., 1966, Prentice-Hall.

I (1-8); II (188-192); III (3-5); IV (84-90, 185-188); V (170-181); VI (185-188); VII (158-161, 179-181, 188-193); VIII (13-18, 165-169); IX (20-25); X (194-200); XI-XII (202-212); XIII (213-219); XIV, XV, XVI (220-235); XVII, XVIII, XIX (170-175).

Zumberge, *Elements of Geology,* 2nd. ed., 1963, Wiley.

I (1-8); II (13-19); III (20-25); V (26-40, 52-62); VI (95-100); VII (154-157); VIII (119-126); IX (103-117); X (127-137); XI (145-152); XII (183-193); XIII (194-200); XIV (202-212); XV (213-219); XVI, XVII (220-236).

QUICK REFERENCE TABLE TO STANDARD TEXTBOOKS

All Arabic figures refer to pages.   See preceding pages for complete titles.

Chapter in Outline	Topic	Bates & Sweet	Branson et al.	Dunbar	Eardley	Emmons et al.	Garrels	Gilluly et al.
1	The Science of Geology	3-10	3-4			1-7	1-13	1-4
2	Our Planet, Earth	11-13 20-23	81-83	50-62	447-452	9-18	1-13 17-22	147-156
3	Interior of the Earth	12-20			247-252	433-441	308-312 318-323 333-349	402-413
4	Vulcanism	35-50	11-47 51-58 292-294		76-95	76-106	225-244 300-304	27-32 358-379
5	Geologic Structures	167-181 191-202	280-292 294-300		39-58 325-334	210-228 270-272 370-399	254-263	108-142 415-449
6	Earthquakes	13	302-318		237-246 252-256	414-431	312-318	385-406
7	Minerals	15-17 96, 190	5-10 47-49		10-19	2-3 60-75 118-125 177-184	21-22 225-226 477-481	5-18 452-497
8	Rocks	35-50 87-104 182-190	49-53 181-210 217-232		22-75 96-104	74-75 108-118 146-177 401-413	22-23 197-217 222-225 245-253 480	20-41 498-509
9	Weathering and Soils	51-58	59-80 214-216		105-115	126-141	24-27	43-58
10	Gravity Movements	59-66	62-63 147-149			192-202	28 49-51	60-62 178-186
11	Streams	67-84 122-135	84-124		119-147	203-251 357	35-88	66-71 188-217

QUICK REFERENCE TABLE TO STANDARD TEXTBOOKS (*Cont.*)

All Arabic figures refer to pages. See preceding pages for complete titles.

Chapter in Outline	Topic	Holmes (Principles)	Holmes (Introduction)	Kummel	Leet & Judson	Longwell & Flint	Longwell *et al.* (Outlines)	Longwell *et al.* (Physical)
1	The Science of Geology	1–13	1–12		1–6	1–11	1–2 9–12	1 8–11 12–14 22–27
2	Our Planet, Earth	14–16 20–35	13–34		19–27	13–25	2–4 8–9	1–6 22
3	Interior of the Earth	16–21 923–959	17–22 35–37		308–320 323–324	404–412	289–293 314–318	14–22 437–449
4	Vulcanism	249–339 1009–1025	9–10 53, 55–57 241–258 409		43–58	79–111	207–243 295–296 330–336	283–293 298 304–342 346–348 452–453 525–533
5	Geologic Structures	195–233 583–591 1109–1192	10, 117 156–158 361–363		248–277	347–374	244–261 271–274 297–314	351–386 454–479
6	Earthquakes	891–922	18 354–367		291–307 311–316	391–412	275–289	392–411
7	Minerals	64–91 435–464	35–105 439–469		31–42 338–353	27–37 468–475	13–23 319–329	511–525 546–559
8	Rocks	55–56 92–141 165–194	40–41 50–105		59–71 91–110 278–290 363–374	37–48 476–482	4–8 24–42 187–195 199–200 261–268	6–8 253–273 293 295–302 413–436 560–576
9	Weathering and Soils	36–40 386–410	75–82		72–90 94	113–131	43–57	28–52
10	Gravity Movements	481–495			123–134	133–151	57–67	54–70

11	Streams	468-475 504-618	368-400		135-160	153-195	68-84 85-102	71-95 97-117 481-499
12	Ground Water	411-434	401-425		161-175	197-211	103-116 201-202	118-139 274-275 342-346
13	Glaciation	619-742	285-324		176-201	227-252	127-155 196	158-189 196-198
14	Swamps and Lakes	668-675			190-191 197	213-226	117-126	141-156
15	Oceans	782-890 934-944	338-353		222-247	281-321	169-186	222-251
16	Wind	743-781	426-438		208-218	265-280	156-168	200-220
17	Maps				375-380	483-491	368-372	577-581
18	Origin of the Earth		28-34		25-30			
19	Evolution of Life	142-155 1193-1250	6, 167-168 173-174	22-51 507-544			197-198	275-276
20	Interpretation of Geologic History	154-164	142-145	1-21 52-71	111-122	49-64	203-205 268-271 359-367	276-279 294-295 386-390
21	Pre-Cambrian Eras		106-129	72-90	198	62-63		
22	Paleozoic Era		130-207	91-214	266-267 329-332	62-63		
23	Mesozoic Era		208-246	215-347	327	62-63		
24	Cenozoic Era		247-337	348-505	333	62-63		189-196

QUICK REFERENCE TABLE TO STANDARD TEXTBOOKS (*Cont.*)

All Arabic figures refer to pages. See preceding pages for complete titles.

Chapter in Outline	Topic	Moore	Putnam	Spencer (Historical)	Spencer (Physical)	Stokes	Zumberge
1	The Science of Geology				3–11 21–55	3–9	1–7
2	Our Planet, Earth	46–47 51 55–57	2–21		12–19	126–139	11–15 21–29
3	Interior of the Earth		219–229		184–213	141–157	62–67 69–71 82–86
4	Vulcanism		38–87		99–116	44–47, 100	37–43 86–99
5	Geologic Structures		118–157 408–427		417–438	42–44, 50–67, 162–164	49–59 70–71 204–205
6	Earthquakes		200–219		184–205	42, 142–143, 153	73–85
7	Minerals		23–37 159–181		79–98	53–55 105–107 228–229	31–37 57–59
8	Rocks	235–238	23, 39–54 89–117		118–159 403–416	35–37	37–38 43–49 57–59
9	Weathering and Soils		231–249		227–239		101–102
10	Gravity Movements		249–257		240–253	66	
11	Streams		258–287		255–277	38–42 325–326	143–161
12	Ground Water		183–199		301–316		67–69 125–142

1
The Science of Geology

Geology is the science of the earth—its composition and structure, its history, and its past plant and animal life. The word geology is derived from the Greek *geo-*, earth, and *logos*, discourse. It was used in its present meaning at least as early as 1605 by Aldrovandus. Geology developed as a science in 1667 through the work of Nicolaus Steno, but its widespread study began about a century later. It became a popular science in Europe and America during the first half of the nineteenth century.

RELATION OF GEOLOGY TO OTHER SCIENCES

Although it is an independent science, geology rests upon a foundation of astronomy, chemistry, physics, and biology. It is closely related to anthropology, geography, and economics. If we are to study the earth, we must consider its origin, its place in the solar system, and its relation to the universe as a whole—these are matters of astronomy. Study of the composition and structure of the earth involves questions of chemistry and physics. The evolution of living things is a common concern of geology and biology; the justification for including the history of life in geology is that the records of that history are found in the rocks. Anthropology, which treats man's biological and cultural history, shares with geology the data of human skeletal remains and primitive artifacts. Geography describes the earth's land surface, water areas, and air, and the present distribution of life, including man and his industries. Finally, both economics and geology are concerned, from different points of view, with iron, coal, oil, and other earth resources.

Mathematics is fundamental to every physical science. A general introduction to geology may be understood by an intelligent student who knows no advanced mathematics; but a working geologist must have a good mathematical training, the amount of mathematics he needs varying with the branch of geology in which he specializes. In order to progress as a geologist, one must also have an ability to write adequate technical reports.

1

BRANCHES OF GEOLOGY

The science is commonly divided into the fields of physical and historical geology. *Physical,* or *dynamic(al), geology* deals with the materials that constitute the earth, the structure and surface features of the earth, and the processes that have given the earth its present structure and appearance. *Historical geology* deals with the history of the earth—its changing face and structure and the changing forms of living things whose remains or traces are found as fossils in the rocks.

Geology is further divided into a number of branches according to (1) the subject matter covered or (2) its industrial or commercial applications.

Branches Based on Subject Matter. *Geochemistry* is the study of the chemistry of rocks and of the waters and atmosphere. *Geodesy* is concerned with measuring the form and size of the earth. *Geomorphology* is the study of land forms, their origin and development. *Geophysics* is the application of the principles of physics to the study of the earth. (*Geomagnetics* is a branch of geophysics concerned with the earth's magnetic fields; another branch is *seismology,* the study of earthquakes.) *Mineralogy* is the study of minerals. (*Crystallography,* in so far as it deals with crystalline minerals—it also deals with nonmineral crystals—may be considered a branch of mineralogy.) *Oceanography* is the study of the oceans and their basins. *Paleontology* is the study of the life of past geologic periods and the evolution of plants and animals whose remains or traces are found in the rocks. (*Paleobotany* deals with plants and *paleozoology* with animals of the geologic past.) *Petrology* is the systematic study of rocks, especially their origin. (It includes *petrography,* which treats of the identification, description, and classification of rocks, and *petrogenesis,* which deals with the origins of various kinds of rocks.) The term *physiography* (or *physical geography*) embraces the fields of geomorphology, meteorology, climatology, and oceanography. *Stratigraphy* is the study of layered rocks, chiefly those of sedimentary origin. *Structural geology* deals with the positions of rock bodies, and with *tectonic geology* interprets the forces causing them to be deformed or broken. Branches of geology pertaining to specific agents and processes include *glacial geology, sedimentology* (which has merged with stratigraphy), and *volcanology.*

Branches Based on Application. *Economic geology* is a broad field, involving the commercial and industrial uses of the resources of the earth. It uses all the principles and techniques of physical and historical geology. *Agricultural geology* is the study of soils, especially of their depletion and erosion. *Engineering geology* is geology applied to the building of dams, reservoirs, highways, bridges, tunnels, irrigation works, and other construction projects. *Hydrology* is the study of surface and underground water. *Mining geology* is geology applied to the finding and extraction of metallic deposits (ores) and nonmetallic resources, such as coal, building stones, clay, etc. *Petroleum geology* is the study of the origin and occurrence of petroleum (oil) and natural gas. *Military geology* is the application of geologic knowledge to warfare.

HISTORY OF GEOLOGY

Throughout the ages man has looked upon the face of the earth with wonder and sometimes, when threatened by earthquakes or erupting volcanoes, with terror. His first attempts to explain the existence and nature of the earth belong to the history of religion.

The first rationalistic speculations of a geologic nature occurred among the Greek natural philosophers. Thales, who died about 550 B.C., seems to have believed the earth to be a flat disk floating on water, the primary substance from which all things are made. His contemporary, Anaximander, pictured the earth as shaped like a cylinder and believed in the evolution of animals and man from fishes. It has been said that he was the first to make a map of the known world. Anaximenes believed the earth to be a disk floating in air. Xenophanes inferred from the fact that fossils of oceanic origin are found on dry land that at one time land and sea were mingled.

The Pythagoreans and Plato believed the earth to be round—because the sphere is a perfect figure. Democritus (fifth century B.C.) believed that the earth and heavenly bodies were spheres formed by the agglomeration of atoms. Aristotle (384–322 B.C.) deduced the sphericity of the earth from the circular shadow cast upon the moon during lunar eclipses and from the differences in apparent positions of the stars as seen in northern and southern latitudes.

Some ancients achieved the realization that the face of the earth
has changed, that land masses, for example, have risen and fallen.
Herodotus remarked on the fact that Egypt's fertile soil was
produced by the recurrent flooding of the Nile.

The Alexandrian Eratosthenes (third century B.C.) calculated
the circumference of the earth, overestimating it by about one-
seventh. He and later geographers, among them Strabo and
Ptolemy, greatly increased geographic knowledge about Europe,
Asia, and Africa.

Pliny the Elder, a Roman naturalist of the first century A.D.,
devoted five books of his 37-book *Historia naturalis* to minerals,
which he described and discussed in a semiscientific way. He may
be considered a martyr to scientific curiosity, for he died of
asphyxiation when he approached too near to Vesuvius in order
to observe the eruption of 79 A.D.

With the revival of interest in science in the sixteenth century,
geologic progress began anew. In an age when fossils were regarded as freaks of nature, Leonardo da Vinci recognized that
they were the remains of plants and animals. The German Georg
Bauer ("Agricola"), who wrote *De re metallica* (1556), may be
considered the father of mineralogy. The first outline of a scientific history of the earth arrived at through observation and inductive reasoning was published in 1667 by the Danish physician
Niels Stensen (Nicolaus Steno).

Modern geology developed, in the late eighteenth century, as
a result of the need for a practical knowledge of rocks and
minerals in the mining districts of northwestern Europe. One
of the great early geologists (he called the science "geognosy")
was Abraham Gottlob Werner (1750–1817). He improved the
classification of minerals but is better remembered as the creator
of the discredited "neptunist" theory that all the rocks of the
earth's crust were precipitated from a universal ocean. This
theory was disproved by Nicholas Desmarest (1782–1815), called
the "father of volcanology," and by Werner's pupils Jean
François D'Aubuisson (1769–1819) and Christian Leopold von
Buch (1774–1853). This prolonged dispute is known as "The
Neptunist-Plutonist Controversy."

James Hutton (1726–1797) is regarded as the founder of scientific geology because of his formulation, in *The Theory of the
Earth,* 1785, of the principle of *uniformitarianism*—the doctrine
that all past changes in the earth's surface are the results of the

operation of the same physical laws that operate today, or, as it is often expressed, that "the present is the key to the past."

Because uniformitarianism presupposed long ages of geologic time, it was rejected by those who still accepted Archbishop Ussher's date for the creation of the world, 4004 B.C. The theory of *catastrophism* of Baron Georges Cuvier (1769–1832) was preferred; this theory taught that at various times in the past all of *catastrophism* of Baron G. L. Cuvier (1769–1832) was preferred; this theory taught that at various times in the past all living things were destroyed by natural catastrophes (like the Biblical Flood) and replaced by a new population. (In spite of his erroneous world view, Cuvier did much valuable work in comparative anatomy and is considered the founder of paleontology.)

The revolutionary theory of uniformitarianism finally won general acceptance, largely through the effective arguments of Sir Charles Lyell, in his *Principles of Geology* (1830–1833). The uniformitarian principle became the cornerstone of geology, which was now able to proceed beyond classification to explanation based on natural laws.

The present view of geologic development, while uniformitarian, recognizes variations in the speed and intensity of geologic processes (as evidenced, for example, by the irregularly spaced cycles of glaciation).

The orderly sequence of fossils in rocks was first recognized by William ("Strata") Smith in England and by Cuvier in the Paris Basin, thus making possible the study of stratigraphy and the making of geologic maps.

The stage was now set for the theory of biologic evolution. As early as 1801, Jean Baptiste Lamarck, the founder of invertebrate paleontology, set forth a theory of evolution, antedating Darwin by half a century. But in the early nineteenth century the contrary views of Cuvier prevailed.

Geologic knowledge has today become so vast that it can only be outlined in a book of this size. The steady accumulation of factual information may be attributed to the use of scientific method and new scientific instruments.

THE SCIENTIFIC METHOD IN GEOLOGY

Geology utilizes, so far as possible, the scientific method. Scientific investigation begins with *observations of nature* and the *collection and classification of data* derived from them. Considering these data and using *inductive reasoning* (i.e., proceeding from the particular to the general), the scientist formulates a *hypothesis,* or tentative explanation of the phenomena observed. This hypothesis is tested by experimentation; or, if experimentation is impossible, it is verified—or perhaps invalidated—by further observation. If the hypothesis seems sufficiently strong, it may come to be referred to as a *theory.* When the theory is generally accepted by other scientists in the field, it acquires the status of a scientific *law.* (It is possible that new observations or experiments may contradict the "law," so that it is replaced by a new formulation which takes account of all the known facts.)

The science of geology has developed under severe handicaps. It is not possible to observe the interior of the earth; man's deepest penetrations of the earth's crust—oil wells—extend only several miles below the surface. Nor is it possible to observe the earth and its inhabitants in past ages. But much can be seen and the field of observation is being extended; it is now possible, for example, to photograph the ocean bottom at great depths.

Furthermore, the scope of experimentation in geology is limited. The geologist cannot create a large-scale earthquake. He must study earthquakes as they occur in nature, although he can obtain some information from minor artificial earthquakes resulting from man-made explosion. He cannot duplicate in the laboratory the full range of pressures that exist below the "skin" of the planet. Still, a remarkable number of valuable experiments have been made by geologists.

There has been accumulated a vast amount of sound geologic knowledge, which is constantly being increased. The present trend in geology is toward the greater use of quantitative data. To an ever increasing extent, geology is becoming an exact science.

TOOLS OF THE GEOLOGIST

Geologists use many aids in their work, including surveying, geophysical, and optical instruments, maps, and literature.

Surveying Instruments. A *plane table* is a drawing board mounted on a tripod. Distances are determined by means of a calibrated telescope, the *alidade,* which is focused upon a measuring stick called a *stadia rod.* The making of large-scale maps requires surveying instruments generally used by engineers, a *transit* being substituted for the alidade and plane table; a very precise transit is known as a *theodolite*. The *Brunton compass* is a hand-sized instrument for measuring angles and directions. Electronic equipment is now used to measure distances in mapping. Satellite geodesy, using artificial satellites and *ballistic cameras,* have revolutionized the techniques of surveying and mapping.

Geophysical Instruments. A *dip needle* is used to measure the magnetic attraction of rocks. A *magnetometer* measures variations in the earth's magnetic field. A *pendulum* and a *gravimeter* measure the force of gravitation as it varies from place to place. Some types of magnetometers and gravimeters are airborne or shipborne. A *seismograph* records natural and artificial earthquake waves. *Geiger* and *scintillation counters* measure radioactivity. Electrical and electromagnetic methods of geophysical prospecting adapt familiar equipment to their special requirements.

Optical Instruments. A *petrographic microscope* is used to study crystals, minerals, and "thin sections" of rocks (about .03 mm. thick) in polarized light. Mineralogists may also use an *electron microscope,* especially in the study of clay minerals, a *phase microscope,* and an *X-ray diffractometer,* both in the identification of minerals and in the study of their atomic structure. The *spectrometer* is another powerful tool used in mineral investigations.

Maps and Literature. *Topographic maps, geologic maps, profiles, cross sections,* and *block diagrams* may be considered tools of the geologist. (See Chapter 17.) The complex literature of geology includes books, journals, government documents, theses, abstracts, index guides, and bibliographies.

GEOLOGY AS A PROFESSION

The profession of geology offers a wide variety of opportunities and attractive rewards in remuneration and prestige. It should appeal to those who enjoy outdoor life, for, although many geologists work indoors most of the time, the field is the geologist's real laboratory. A combination of both kinds of work, preferably arranged according to the season, often proves very satisfactory. But one disadvantage should be mentioned: the necessity of moving one's living quarters frequently and often living in out-of-the-way places.

Most American geologists are employed in the world-wide petroleum industry; the American Association of Petroleum Geologists is the largest organization of geologists. Many petroleum geologists work for the major oil companies, some for the independents, and still others for firms that perform geophysical, surveying, or other services under contract. Employment abroad in the petroleum industry pays more than comparable work in the United States and attracts many young, unmarried college graduates.

Some experienced petroleum geologists operate their own offices as consultants. They examine properties and supervise the drilling of wells. Part of their efforts may be devoted to locating and mapping structures in which oil or gas may occur and then attempting to arrange for the disposal of the mineral rights to an oil company under a leasing agreement.

Although many geologists are employed on the regular staffs of large mining companies, most of the "hard rock" geologists act as independent consultants. In this capacity they may determine whether a certain property should be bought or developed; they may map rocks and structures in order to decide where further exploration should be conducted; they may estimate, for investment or tax purposes, the reserves of available ore.

Recently, many "soft rock" geologists, who have concentrated on sedimentary (layered) rocks and would formerly have found employment in the petroleum industry, have been attracted by the uranium mining industry. The unequal distribution of underground-water resources in an era of expanding population and industry offers greatly enlarged opportunities for geologists in a private or public capacity.

Among the branches of geology that have been growing faster than the rest are lunar geology, marine geology, mineral economics (of value to banks, insurance companies, and governmental agencies), engineering geology (in the planning of building sites), and especially secondary-school teaching. Women geologists are mostly employed in teaching, research, librarianship, and laboratory work.

The chief government agency employing geologists is the United States Geological Survey. The activities of this important and highly respected organization include mapping and classifying public land, promoting conservation, and doing pure research in every phase of geology. The Water Resources Branch is the largest division of the United States Geological Survey. Another important government agency that hires geologists is the United States Bureau of Reclamation. Besides the federal agencies, there are state and local agencies that employ geologists for such activities as surveying and mapping.

Geologic research is also carried on by institutes founded for that purpose and by universities. Museums, some of which conduct expeditions to the far corners of the globe, employ many geologists. Among the varied activities of research geologists are those of investigating of earthquakes, making synthetic minerals, and reconstructing dinosaur skeletons.

Further information regarding professional opportunities in geology may be obtained from the American Geological Institute, 1444 N Street, Washington, D.C. 20005.

REVIEW QUESTIONS

1. Give a suitable definition of geology and name its two principal subdivisions.
2. Name the other sciences upon which geology depends.
3. Define the following branches of geology: petrology, seismology, geomorphology, paleontology, hydrology.
4. Describe some of the chief types of work done by geologists.
5. Explain the significance of uniformitarianism in the history of geology.

PART I
Physical Geology

2
Our Planet, Earth

The origin of the earth is of considerable interest to geologists even though that problem might seem to belong to *cosmogony*, more properly a branch of astronomy. As students of geology we concentrate our attention upon the period of time after the solidification of the earth's molten surface had produced the first rocks.

Nor is the relation of the earth to the rest of the universe a matter for detailed investigation by geologists as such. Nevertheless, before beginning the study of the earth itself, we should briefly consider its place in the universe.

THE EARTH AND THE UNIVERSE

The universe, as we know it, is composed of innumerable *galaxies,* or star clusters. The galaxy in which we live, the Milky Way, is a disk-shaped revolving cluster of some 30 billion stars of varying size and brightness. One of these stars, of modest size and brightness and nearer the edge than the center of the galaxy, is our sun.

The sun is the center of the *solar system,* in which the largest solid bodies that revolve about the sun are called *planets.* The nine planets, in the order of their proximity to the sun, are Mercury, Venus, Earth, Mars, Jupiter, Saturn, Uranus, Neptune, and Pluto. Table 1 gives a simplified comparison of the sun, moon, and planets. An unknown number of smaller bodies also revolve about the sun; if they are large enough to be seen (telescopically) and named, they are called *asteroids* or *planetoids.* Many very small bodies called *meteorites* enter the earth's atmosphere daily. (The earth has been struck by meteorites or asteroids large enough to make huge craters.) The huge but tenuous objects called *comets* also belong to the solar system.

Most of the planets have one or more *satellites* revolving about them. The earth's natural satellite, the moon, with a diameter of 2,160 miles, revolves about the earth at an average distance of a little less than 240 thousand miles. Because the moon makes one rotation about its axis in the same time (about 27⅓ days) that it makes one revolution about the earth, it turns the same face

TABLE 1 *

CHARACTERISTICS OF THE SUN, MOON, AND PLANETS

	Diameter		Volume	Density	Mass	Distance from Sun
	(miles)	(earth = 1)	(earth = 1)	(water = 1)	(earth = 1)	(million miles)
Sun	864,000	109	1,300,000	1.4	332,000	—
Mercury	3,000	0.38	0.055	3.8	0.056	36
Venus	7,600	0.96	0.88	4.9	0.80	67
Earth	7,920	1.00	1.00	5.5	1.00	93
Mars	4,200	0.53	0.15	4.0	0.11	142
Jupiter	87,000	10.9	1,325	1.3	318	483
Saturn	71,500	9.0	730	0.7	95	886
Uranus	29,400	3.7	50	1.3	15	1,780
Neptune	28,000	3.5	43	1.6	17	2,790
Pluto	7,600	0.96	0.88	5.8	0.93	3,670
Moon	2,160	0.27	0.02	3.3	0.012	93

* Table prepared by Professor Theodore A. Smits for second edition of *Making Friends with the Stars* by Arthur J. Zaade, published by Barnes & Noble, Inc.

to the earth at all times. (But it wobbles sufficiently to enable us to see 59 per cent of its surface at one time or another.) The most noteworthy physical effect of the moon upon the earth is the creation of tides (see Chapter 15).

SHAPE OF THE EARTH

The earth is a *geoid,* a *triaxial ellipsoid,* nearly spherical but slightly flattened at the poles. The diameter from pole to pole is about 27 miles less than the average distance through the equator, which has two unequal axes. Curious small bulges make four "corners" at Ireland, off Peru, south of Africa, and near New Guinea. The vertical difference between the highest mountain peak (Everest, over 29,000 feet) and the greatest known depth of ocean (near the Philippine island of Mindanao, 36,560 feet) is only a little more than 12 miles.

The spherical shape of the earth accounts for the following phenomena noted in antiquity: the apparent submergence of ships putting out to sea; the circular shadow of the earth cast upon the moon during lunar eclipses; and the changing elevation of the North Star in relation to the place from which it is observed. Now the curvature of the earth can be clearly seen in high-altitude photographs.

SIZE OF THE EARTH

The earth has a polar diameter of about 7,900 miles and an equatorial diameter of about 7,927 miles. Its circumference, around the equator, is approximately 24,900 miles. The area of the earth's surface is about 197 million square miles, of which about 71 per cent is covered by oceans. The volume of the earth is a little more than 250 billion cubic miles, and its mass has been estimated at about 6,600 quintillion (6,600,000,000,000,000,-000,000) tons.

MOVEMENTS OF THE EARTH

The earth moves in a number of directions at the same time. It rotates on its axis (which extends through the poles), and the duration of one rotation (relative to the sun) has become one of our basic measurements of time, the solar day. The velocity of rotation at the equator is about 1,037 miles per hour; at the poles it is, of course, zero.

Besides its rotation, the earth has a slight wobbling motion (called *precession*) which causes its axis to describe a cone-shaped figure once in about 25,800 years.

The earth also revolves about the sun at an average velocity of about 18.5 miles per second, completing one revolution in a little more than 365¼ days, thus providing us with another basic measurement of time, the solar year. The earth's orbit is elliptical, its distance from the sun varying from about 91.5 to about 94.5 million miles.

The axis of the earth is inclined at an angle of 23.5 degrees, so that each hemisphere is tilted toward the sun during half of the year and away from it during the other half, thus producing the seasons.

The entire solar system is speeding through space toward the star Vega at a velocity of 12 miles per second. Our galaxy, furthermore, apparently rotates on an axis and has an independent movement away from other galaxies.

MAJOR DIVISIONS OF THE EARTH

Three zones, corresponding to the three states of matter (solid, liquid, gas), constitute the globe we know as the earth. The solid central zone is the *lithosphere*. Cradled in the ocean basins and distributed across the surface of the land is the zone of water, the *hydrosphere*. Surrounding them both is a gaseous envelope, the *atmosphere*.

The boundaries between the three zones are not perfectly sharp; there is some mingling of air and water, of air and rock, of water and rock.

Lithosphere. The nature of the lithosphere—the earth's crust and interior—will be discussed in Chapter 3. Here we shall mention some important processes and relief features of the lithosphere.

Processes Within the Lithosphere. Within the lithosphere act the physical and chemical forces that produce *vulcanism* and elevate portions of the crust, forming land masses and making possible the many forms of life on land. Within the lithosphere, too, resides most of the force of the earth's gravity which holds the hydrosphere and atmosphere captive. Fluids and gases—mostly water and air—occupy pores and larger cavities within the outer portions of the crust. In regions where freezing occurs, small quantities of water in fractures and other open spaces in rocks alter their contours by the process of *weathering*. Mountains are slowly leveled and other features are altered by *erosion,* the wearing effect of wind, moving water, and ice (glaciers).

Relief Features. These are the elements of topography that give height and depth to the surface of the lithosphere.

First-Order Relief Features. The *continents* and *ocean basins* constitute the major irregularities in the almost smooth form of the lithosphere. The continents are the exposed areas of the true continental masses, the hearts of which consist of oval or shield-shaped areas of very ancient and greatly altered rock; these areas are known as *shields.* The continents extend as *continental shelves* beneath the shallower fringes of the oceans; the outer margins of the continents (*continental slopes*) drop steeply down into the actual ocean basins. Intermittently the continental shelves have been slowly laid bare and then slowly covered again by water; thus the shore lines of the continents have changed throughout the geologic past, as described in Part II on Historical Geology (see p. 191). The continents and ocean basins are presumed to be kept in balance by a principle called *isostasy*, whereby the lighter granitic layer of the continents "floats" in the heavier basaltic layer which constitutes the ocean basins and underlies the continents.

One of the chief current problems in geology is that of *continental drift*. It is concerned with whether the continents and ocean basins have always been permanently situated relative to one another, or if they have moved (and may still be moving) (see p. 47, 128).

Second-Order Relief Features. Plains, plateaus, and *mountains* constitute the next most conspicuous aspects of topography. Both plains and plateaus are underlain by flat-lying rocks, the difference between them being merely a matter of elevation. Mountains may possess any of several kinds of structure. Second-order relief features exist within the ocean basins just as they do on land; abrupt, narrow mountain chains called *ridges* and long, narrow troughs called *deeps* contribute to the ruggedness of the sea floor (see Chapter 15). Especially interesting are the *submarine canyons* of the continental shelves, which rival any canyons found on dry land and which have never been adequately explained.

Third-Order Relief Features. These are features of the landscape of lesser importance than those mentioned above. They include a great variety of scenic effects such as glacial troughs (U-shaped valleys), sand dunes, lava flows, and fault scarps, due, in corresponding order, to erosion, deposition, vulcanism, and earth movements.

Hydrosphere. A sphere of water, containing absorbed air and carrying particles of rock as sediment, surrounds the earth. Most of it lies within the ocean basins. (The extent and shape of the seas have varied greatly with the rising and sinking of portions of the continents.) Water also appears on the surface of the land in the form of lakes and running streams, which are important agents of erosion and transportation, and sites of deposition. A relatively small amount of the earth's water penetrates into the lithosphere; nevertheless, such *ground water* is of immense importance.

Atmosphere. The envelope of air that embraces our planet contains absorbed water and small quantities of rock as dust, which may act as centers for the condensation of water vapor as clouds or fog. The chief component (78 per cent) of the atmosphere is nitrogen, but this gas is almost inert, as are the very small amounts of argon, neon, helium, krypton, xenon, and other rare gases. The gases significant to man, and significant geologically, are oxygen (21 per cent) and carbon dioxide. Water vapor (measured as *humidity*) is present in the air in amounts that vary with place and time.

Energized by the heat of the sun, the *hydrologic cycle* involves the evaporation of water, mainly from the oceans, its circulation by air currents over the continents, its precipitation as rain or snow, and the ultimate return of most of it to the sea under the influence of gravity.

GEOLOGIC PROCESSES

The geologic processes operating upon and within the crust of the earth may be grouped under three main headings: gradation, vulcanism, and diastrophism.

Gradation. This term encompasses the opposing processes of degradation and aggradation. Weathering, the decomposition and disintegration of rocks, can be considered part of the process of gradation.

DEGRADATION. This process, also called *erosion*, is the wearing down of rocks by water, ice, and wind.

AGGRADATION. This process, also called *deposition*, is the building up of rock layers by the accumulation of sediment, which is deposited by the action of water, ice, and wind.

Vulcanism. This term refers to all movements of molten rock and the formation of solid rock from a molten state both within the lithosphere and on the surface.

Diastrophism. Included in this term are all movements of the solid parts of the earth, resulting in its displacement (faulting) or deformation (folding). The complex processes of metamorphism belong in large part at least under this heading, although vulcanism is also involved.

REVIEW QUESTIONS

1. Name the nine planets in order of distance from the sun.
2. Name the other constituents of the solar system.
3. Why does the moon always turn the same face to the earth?
4. Why is the shape of the earth called an oblate spheroid?
5. State four lines of evidence that the earth is round.
6. What are the movements of the earth?
7. Name the three great zones that make up the earth.
8. Name the three major geologic processes.

3
Interior of the Earth

Geologists have constructed a model of the earth that seems to correspond to nearly all the data discovered about its interior as revealed mainly through the study of earthquake records. However, alternative interpretations are possible, and modifications of the contemporary model are certain to result as knowledge increases.

EVIDENCE OF VARIABLE INTERIOR

Several lines of evidence indicate that the interior of the earth is variable, consisting of concentric shells which differ in composition, density, elasticity, and perhaps state.

Earthquake Waves. The behavior of earthquake (*seismic*) waves shows clearly that the earth is zoned. As they travel from one zone to another, the waves change in velocity according to the nature of the material through which they pass. They are also reflected and refracted (bent) at the boundaries between the zones; these rather sharp breaks are called *discontinuities*.

Specific Gravity of the Earth. Dividing the mass of the earth by its volume gives the specific gravity, or density, as 5.516—i.e., a little over 5.5 times as heavy as an equal bulk of water. Since the surface rocks have specific gravities ranging from 2.6 to 3.0, the buried rocks must have much greater specific gravities.

Shape of the Earth. The magnitude of the bulge of the earth at the equator, which is due to its rotation, indicates that the earth has a very heavy core and does not become regularly more dense from the surface to the center.

Precession and Tides. Measurement of the precession, or angle through which the tilt of the earth's axis slowly changes, and of the body tides in the solid earth, caused by the gravitational pull of the sun and the moon, also proves the existence of a separate, very heavy core.

CRUST

The crust of the earth—so named more than a century ago, when our planet was believed to be a great molten ball covered by a thin shell of rock—is today considered to be only the outer part of the solid lithosphere, composed mainly of rocks similar to those visible at the surface, and extending down 20–30 miles to the clearly defined level referred to as the *Mohorovičić* (or *Moho* or *M-*) *discontinuity.*

All that we can actually observe of the earth's interior is confined to the crust—and the outer part of the crust, at that. The deepest oil wells penetrate little more than four miles; the deepest mine shafts extend downward less than 10,000 feet; and the Grand Canyon of the Colorado River is only about a mile deep. Mountainous areas that have been greatly uplifted and deeply eroded provide us with the most satisfactory direct view of rocks as they previously existed at depths of several miles.

Structure of the Crust. The earth's rocky crust, beneath the thin veneer of sediments present in many places, has a twofold and in many ways a contrasting nature; it is composed of (1) the continental blocks and (2) the ocean basins.

CONTINENTS. As can be seen in the field, granite is the most abundant primary rock of the continents. Furthermore, earthquake waves travel through the outer part of the bedrock of the continents at a rate equal to the velocity at which they travel in granite (as measured experimentally). This zone is therefore called the *granitic layer,* or *sial* (from its chemical content which is high in *si*licon and *al*uminum); it is generally 6–9 miles (10–15 kilometers) thick.

An irregular discontinuity may separate this zone from the one beneath, though a gradual transition seems more probable. In the lower zone earthquake waves move more rapidly, indicating a denser kind of rock, corresponding to basalt. This zone is therefore called the *basaltic substratum,* or *sima* (from its chemical content which is high in *si*licon and *ma*gnesium); it extends to a depth of 18–24 miles (30–40 kilometers) below the surface, and even deeper (as much as 36 miles, or about 60 kilometers) beneath active mountain belts.

OCEAN BASINS. The continental (granitic) type of material is absent from the Pacific Ocean basin and seems to be nearly or entirely absent from the other ocean basins. There, instead, is seen, where exposed in scattered islands, the heavier and darker rock called *basalt;* its widespread presence throughout the ocean basins is inferred from the higher velocity of earthquake waves transmitted under the oceans. The irregular bottom of the lower (oceanic) zone is the Mohorovičić discontinuity, which lies 6–8 miles (10–13 kilometers) below sea level and marks the base of the crust.

Mountain Roots. This description of a double layer of rock—granite above and basalt beneath, the granite being missing from the ocean basins—is complicated by the presence of mountains. The failure of certain earthquake waves to pass beneath huge granitic mountain ranges, and the reduced attraction of gravity near such mountain masses (indicated by the deflection of a plumb bob, the swing of a delicate clock pendulum, and the lengthening of the spring in a gravity meter) suggest that these mountains reach down to considerable depths—having "roots," as it were, in the underlying basalt. Like an iceberg's, their submerged part is greater than their exposed part; the granitic zone under mountains may be as much as four times as thick as it is under plains.

Isostasy. The theory of *isostasy* (from Greek words meaning "equal standing") is closely concerned with the penetration of the basaltic substratum by deep-seated granite mountains. A typical mountain region stands high, it is reasoned, because it is the uppermost part of an enormous mass of relatively light rock (granite), most of which is deep-seated. The mountains thus balance the lower-standing regions on both sides, where heavier rock (basalt) is much closer to the surface. Similarly, the granitic continents stand above the basaltic ocean basins.

At some given depth, however, the various bodies of rock in the earth's crust stand in equilibrium with one another; at this depth they all weigh the same amount for equal areas—the light columns being longer (vertically), the heavy ones being shorter. The depth at which this balance exists is called the *level of compensation.* The hypothesis of Pratt puts it at a uniform depth, estimated to be 37–62 miles (60–100 kilometers); that of Airy makes it an irregular boundary corresponding to the density of the given rock column. The M-discontinuity at the bottom of the crust is probably the actual level of compensation.

As rock is removed by erosion from the high places, it accumulates in the low places; also, lava pours out of the earth and piles up on the surface. The strength and rigidity of the earth seem sufficient to permit such activity to go on for some time without any change in the equilibrium of the crust, as shown by the existence of unbalanced areas (*anomalies*) and broad erosion surfaces of considerable duration. Finally, however, the overloaded part of the crust apparently begins to sink. The heavy rock at the level of compensation is displaced to one side by plastic flow (resulting from the great pressure and aided by compression within the crust) and rises beneath the column of lighter rock, pushing it slowly upward. This process of adjustment is called *isostatic compensation*. Perhaps in this way continents and mountain ranges are renewed from one geologic generation to another.

Temperature and Pressure. Both temperature and pressure increase with depth, though probably not at a uniform rate. The change in temperature per unit of depth is the *geothermal gradient*. It averages about 1 degree Fahrenheit for each 60 feet of descent, but variations from this value are large, a more rapid increase occurring in recently deformed rock, a less rapid increase in old, stable areas. The geothermal gradient in young, unstable regions, such as Yellowstone Park, is very steep.

Not far below the surface, the temperature of the rocks is such that at the surface they would melt, but the pressure of the overlying material prevents their melting, except locally. Rocks of the general composition of granite are about three times as radioactive as those with the mineral make-up of basalt; therefore, the upper part of the crust is believed to supply most of the heat due to radioactivity. Because the rocks near the surface are poorer conductors of heat than those farther down, the temperature gradient declines with depth. The difference in rock types within the crust—due to variation in composition and compaction—results in a range of density from that of granite at the surface (specific gravity about 2.65) to that of basalt (about 3.00) before the bottom of the crust is reached.

MANTLE

Between the crust of the earth and the core is the *mantle*. This consists of two, or perhaps three, major zones presumed to be composed of rocky (silicate, sulfide, oxide) material under substantial pressure, adequate to keep it from melting at the high temperatures that prevail there. The boundary between the mantle and the core, at the depth of 1,800 miles (2,900 kilometers), is known as the *Wiechert-Gutenberg discontinuity*.

In density and in its ability to transmit earthquake waves, the outer part of the mantle corresponds to the heavy rock called *peridotite,* having a specific gravity that increases downward from 3.0 to 4.5. The inner part of the mantle may owe its greater density merely to increase of pressure with depth, but it may be composed of material with a composition similar to that of the variety of meteorite known as *pallasite*—a combination of silicate mineral and metal; the specific gravity of this lower part of the mantle increases from 4.5 to 8.0 at the outside of the core.

CORE

The *core*—having a diameter (4,300 miles, or 6,900 kilometers) a little over half that of the earth and a volume about one-eighth that of the earth—is quite unlike the outer zones. Certain earthquake waves (S waves), which are able to travel only through solid bodies, do not pass through the core. Other waves (P waves), which travel through both solids and liquids but more rapidly through solids, slow down and are sharply refracted when they enter the core but speed up again after they pass through the center of the core. It is necessary to infer, then, that the outer core is molten and that—since it is under greater pressure than the material above—it must be composed of a different kind of material. It also seems necessary to conclude that the inner core is solid and is composed of material different from that of the outer core.

The average density of the core is probably 12 or more. (Some estimates say 9 or 10, others 15.) Furthermore, the earth is a giant magnet. These facts suggest a similarity between the outer core and metallic (iron-nickel-cobalt) meteorites, which are heavy, magnetic, and more easily fusible than ordinary rock. Swirling currents of molten iron are believed to exist in the outer part of the core and to be responsible for fluctuations in the earth's magnetic field.

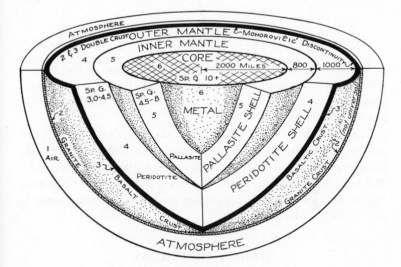

Fig. 1—Interior of the earth. (By permission from *Geology Principles and Processes,* 4th ed., by Emmons, Thiel, Stauffer, and Allison. Copyright, 1955. McGraw-Hill Book Co., Inc.)

The outer core is 1,360 miles (2,267 kilometers) thick, and the inner core has a radius of 790 miles (1,317 kilometers). At the very center the density may be above 17, and the pressure may be more than 3 million times what it is at the surface of the ground.

REVIEW QUESTIONS

1. How can the average specific gravity of the earth be more than 5.5 while that of the visible rocks is not over 3.0?
2. What are the boundaries between the earth's zones called?
3. Describe how the continents differ from the ocean basins.
4. Why are light rocks believed to extend to greater depths beneath mountain ranges than beneath low plains?
5. Why do isostatic anomalies exist?
6. What does the geothermal gradient mean in regard to the interior of the earth?
7. Describe the probable nature of the mantle zone.
8. Describe the probable nature of the earth's core.

4
Vulcanism

The term *vulcanism* is derived from the name of the Roman god of fire, Vulcan. It denotes one of the major geologic processes and covers the origin, movement, and solidification of molten rock.

Most vulcanism takes place below the earth's surface. Underground molten rock is called *magma*. On cooling, it forms the primary, or igneous, rocks, and may reach the surface in fissure and volcanic eruptions, in which cases it is called *lava*. The term vulcanism (*volcanism*) is sometimes used in a restricted sense to refer only to volcanic activity.

ORIGIN OF MAGMA

The question arises: Are the molten rocks constituting magma subject to greater heat than the surrounding rocks, are they of different composition, or is there some other reason for their molten state?

The source of the heat that creates magma is a matter of speculation. At a certain distance below the surface, the temperature is such that all rocks would be molten except for the pressure of the rocks above them. A reduction of pressure on rock subjected to a high temperature could cause this rock to melt. (But usually a rise in temperature is believed to occur when rocks melt.)

The existence of magma is not to be entirely or largely explained by differences in composition of rocks, for rocks of the same composition are found at the same depth in both the solid and the molten states.

A number of possible sources of the heat creating the magma are described below.

Original Heat. Rocks are very poor conductors of heat, and the loss of heat from the earth's interior, apart from that escaping through surface openings, is extremely small. If the earth was at one time an incandescent ball of fire, a molten sphere, or even a hot solid sphere, some of the original heat may still remain. But this residual heat would affect the entire crust equally.

Compaction and Contraction. If the earth grew initially by the accretion of small particles or bodies, no matter how cool, it would develop considerable internal heat through the slow compaction of the material (under the pressure of gravity), for pressure creates heat. Contraction of the cooling planet, increasing internal pressure, might maintain or increase the earth's heat. Also, contraction associated with the folding of layers of rock (forming mountains) would generate large quantities of heat.

Radioactivity. Certain unstable chemical elements break down spontaneously, providing energy that is a likely source of all the heat necessary to explain the phenomena of vulcanism.

These radioactive elements include all those heavier and more complex (having higher atomic numbers) than lead, as well as many *isotopes* (atoms of a single element but different in weight) of lighter elements. Uranium 238, thorium 232, and uranium 235 (sometimes referred to as actinouranium, the key material for the utilization of nuclear energy) are radioactive isotopes whose disintegration sets off three series of radioactive atoms. As each isotope is broken down, it forms a "daughter element," which decays, in turn, until each of the three "distintegration series" of radioactive atoms culminates in lead (Pb–206, 208, 207, respectively), which is entirely stable. The inert gas helium is given off as a by-product. Potassium, a common element in many rocks, is geologically the most important of the radioactive elements that do not belong to one of these regular series.

Radioactivity causes the nucleus of an atom to disintegrate at a uniform rate which is not affected by heat or pressure. Half of a given weight of the atom disintegrates in a unit of time that is constant for that substance. This is called the *half-life,* and among the different elements it can be as short as 3 ten-millionths of a second (polonium 212) or as long as 13,900,000,000 years (thorium 232). These transformations are accompanied by the emission of energy of four kinds, as follows:

1. *Alpha radiation*—atoms of helium which have lost their two electrons (negative charges) and hence are particles having positive charges.

2. *Beta radiation*—electrons.

3. *Gamma radiation*—electromagnetic radiation resembling X rays and light rays, but of shorter wave length.

4. *Heat*—an appreciable amount. Local concentration of heat from radioactivity may melt rock to produce magma. The earth, moreover, may actually be getting hotter on the inside rather than cooler, as was formerly thought. (See Chapter 18 on the origin of the earth.)

NATURE OF MAGMA

Magma is the hot mother liquid of the igneous rocks. It is a melt of rock that is mainly silicate in composition. In addition, it typically contains up to 11 per cent steam and other gases dissolved under pressure, and suspended crystals already formed. The temperature of magma ranges from 500 to 1,400 degrees C (900–2,500 degrees F). Magma either originates from the melting of rocks of various chemical compositions (chiefly granitic and basaltic) or separates from a homogeneous solution in fractions of unlike kinds by a process called *magmatic differentiation*. This process would explain the different kinds of igneous rock. Magma may also change by later chemical reactions with surrounding rocks, or by the mingling of two or more magmas of different composition.

MOVEMENTS OF MAGMA

Being lighter and more mobile than solid rock, magma tends to rise in the crust of the earth, forced up by the exceedingly great pressure upon it of the surrounding rock. Under conditions of mountain formation, the magma may simply be squeezed upward from deep reservoirs called *magma chambers*. Expanding as it reaches positions of lower pressure, the magma releases some of its gases; by means of these corrosive gases a magma may eat its way upward. A magma may also, by heat and mechanical shattering, pry off and engulf huge masses of rock, a process called *magmatic stoping*. The inclusions, if not assimilated, are called *xenoliths* (*xenos,* foreign); partly assimilated fragments, drawn out into wavy sheets, usually with irregular and poorly defined boundaries, are known as *schlieren*.

When it arrives at depths shallow enough for extensive cracks to exist in the adjacent rock, magma begins to move more readily. It emerges as *lava* when it reaches the surface, having lost most of its volatile components. But magma may cool sufficiently to solidify at any point along its upward course, and many magma bodies cease to move while still at considerable depths. Whether formed from magma beneath the surface of the earth or from lava upon it, the solid produce of once-molten rock is an igneous rock.

Intrusive igneous rocks are those that have formed within the crust, where they are surrounded by older rock, into which they came as intruders, or invaders. *Extrusive* igneous rocks are those that have formed from cooling lava at the surface of the earth.

Intrusive Igneous Bodies. Intrusive igneous rock occurring in the form of *plutons* (from Pluto, Greek god of the underworld), which result from the cooling of magma underground, are classified by name on the basis of (1) their mineral composition, which depends upon their chemical composition, and (2) their texture, which depends upon their geologic occurrence (see Chapter 8). Intrusive bodies, regardless of what kind of rock they may consist of, are classified according to their geologic occurrence, involving (1) their size, (2) their shape, (3) their position, and (4) their relation to the enclosing rock. A combination of these factors provides a number of types of *igneous intrusions,* or plutons. Plutons are generally classified as *discordant* and *concordant.**

DISCORDANT PLUTONS. When a pluton cuts across the structure of the older rock in which it lies, it is said to be *discordant.* The most important of all intrusions are the batholiths, most of which are discordant plutons.

Batholiths. If an igneous intrusion has a surface exposure of more than 40 square miles, it is called a *batholith.* Batholiths usually broaden toward the base (though, for all we know, some may narrow at the bottom), and their full depth is not known. Batholiths doubtless supply the magma that forms smaller intrusive bodies at higher levels in the crust.

Batholiths always originate during periods of mountain formation during which intense crumpling has taken place. They are

* In the previous chapter the crust and the mantle of the earth were described as solid, and the outer core as consisting of molten rock. The term *magma* is not applied to the molten outer core, but to pockets of molten rock in the crust and upper mantle which sometimes reach the surface.

elongated and parallel to mountain ranges. The roof of a batholith is irregular; a domelike extension into the rocks above is called a *cupola;* downward projections of the rock into the batholith are called *roof pendants.*

Batholiths are mostly granitic and are fairly uniform in composition throughout. Because of their size they have cooled very slowly over a long period of time, creating coarse-textured rock.

EXAMPLE: The most extensive exposed batholith is the Coast Range batholith of British Columbia, more than 1,000 miles long and in places over 100 miles in width.

Stocks. Stocks are discordant igneous intrusions having a surface exposure of less than 40 square miles, differing from batholiths only in being smaller. Most stocks are probably the cupolas of hidden batholiths. Circular or elliptical stocks may have been vents feeding former volcanoes.

EXAMPLE: The Spanish Peaks in southern Colorado are twin stocks of unusual symmetry.

Volcanic Necks. Volcanic necks, also called *volcanic plugs,* are vertical cylindrical bodies of igneous rock ranging up to a mile in diameter. They are composed of solidified lava which once filled the conduits of volcanoes that have been eroded away, leaving the more resistant plug standing high on the landscape.

Volcanic necks have a columnar structure, due to the shrinkage cracks that appeared in the lava as it solidified.

EXAMPLE: Shiprock in northwestern New Mexico is a sharply eroded volcanic neck rising more than 1,300 feet above the plateau surface.

Dikes. Tabular-shaped (thin and flat) discordant plutons are called *dikes.* They are composed of hardened lava that once flowed upward through fissures which either already existed or were opened by the force of the magma and which were sometimes widened by the corrosive magma. A dike is rarely more than a few feet wide, but may be many miles in length. In places dikes radiate from a volcanic neck or other type of central vent; they may radiate like spokes from a wheel or they may form parallel, crescent-shaped, concentric, or intersecting patterns. Such groups of dikes are referred to as *dike swarms.* A vertical concentric system is called a *ring dike;* if they slant steeply toward the center, they constitute a *cone sheet.*

EXAMPLE: One of the largest known dikes is the Cleveland dike in northern England, which can be traced continuously more than 100 miles as a nearly vertical wall.

CONCORDANT PLUTONS. When the margins of a pluton parallel the layering or any other directional structure of the surrounding rock, it is said to be concordant. Concordant plutons are generally simpler in structure than those that are discordant.

Sills. Resembling dikes in their tabular shape, variation of size, and occurrence in swarms, sills differ only by being parallel to the enclosing rock. They do not have to be horizontal—they may even be vertical if the host rock has been tilted vertically. Most sills are connected with dikes. Sills are sometimes referred to as *intrusive sheets.*

EXAMPLE: The Palisades of the Hudson River is a line of cliffs resulting from the erosion of a gently inclined sill more than 900 feet thick.

Laccoliths. There is no sharp distinction between a sill and a laccolith (Greek *lakkos,* cistern). A laccolith is a sill that is thicker in the center and thins outward in all directions. Laccoliths vary in shape but normally have a flat base and a convex upper surface, and since they have a central feeding conduit through which the magma ascended, a vertical section resembles a mushroom. In general, sills are formed of the more fluid igneous rock types, such as basalt, whereas laccoliths owe their unusual form to the greater viscosity of the more siliceous magmas.

EXAMPLE: The classic examples of laccoliths, though smaller than many others, are those of the Henry Mountains in southern Utah.

Extrusive Igneous Activity and Products. The prolonged upward movement of magma toward the surface of the earth is facilitated by the presence of enough volatiles (gases, mostly steam, and liquids, principally water) to keep it fluid and enough heat to keep it molten. By the time it reaches the surface, however, it has lost a large proportion of its volatiles. It is now called lava, and it solidifies when cold to become extrusive igneous rock. Other volcanic substances may be blown out upon the surface of the ground. Volcanoes are the most dramatic and interesting of extrusive phenomena, but quantitatively they represent a relatively minor aspect.

FISSURE ERUPTIONS. Most of the great lava-covered areas of the world have been formed by outpourings along extensive cracks in the earth's surface known as *fissures,* hence the term *fissure eruptions.* Often associated with such fissures are volcanoes at isolated vents from which lava issues, but fissure eruptions do not

U. S. Geological Survey   Balsley

Fig. 2—Volcanic neck or laccolith. Devils Tower, Wyoming.

require the presence of volcanoes. A group of exceptionally deep fissures constitute a *rift zone.*

EXAMPLES: Regions of outstanding fissure eruptions include the Columbia Plateau in the northwestern part of the United States, the Paraná Basin of South America, and the Deccan Plateau of India. The present volcanoes of Hawaii may rest upon a substantial bed of earlier fissure eruptions.

Because the material of fissure eruptions consists principally of basalt, which often flows out upon the ground in such vast quantities as to build up great thicknesses of horizontal lava sheets, the resulting rocks are known as *plateau,* or *flood, basalts.* The lava of such flows has been seen to move as fast as 12 miles per hour and as far as 60 miles.

VOLCANOES. A *volcano* is a central vent or close group of conduits by which heated rock material emerges from the interior as a *central eruption.* As lava and solid fragments contained in it accumulate around the opening, they build up a symmetrical *cone,* a conical hill or mountain with a funnel-shaped depression, or *crater,* in its center. The largest volcanoes constitute some of the world's loftiest peaks.

Although volcanoes furnish less than 0.1 per cent of the total volume of known igneous rocks, they are of outstanding significance in the study of geology because they provide open-air laboratories for observing nature in action. Volcanoes have been important in human history as destroyers of human life and

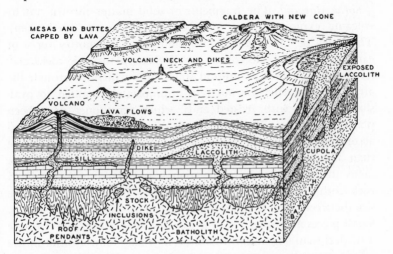

FIG. 3—Structural relations of intrusive and extrusive igneous bodies. (*After F. P. Young.*) (By permission from *Geology Principles and Processes,* 4th ed., by Emmons, Thiel, Stauffer, and Allison. Copyright, 1955. McGraw-Hill Book Co., Inc.)

property but also as sources of fertile soil. Alive or dead, they are awesome scenic wonders.

Volcanic Eruptions. Although volcanic activity at a given site is continuous from birth to dormancy, the visible effects often appear intermittently. At a given time either an explosive or a quiet type of vulcanism predominates, but the kind and intensity of activity of the volcano may change from one eruption to another, and sometimes it is cyclic. The early stages of an eruption are frequently marked by preliminary earthquakes, loud rumblings, cracking of the ground, emptying of lakes, and the appearance of hot springs, and these phenomena may continue throughout the eruption. Torrential rains due to the condensation of moisture in the atmosphere are a common accompaniment of volcanic eruptions.

Volcanic Material. All three states of matter—solid, liquid, and gas—are ejected from volcanoes. The nature of a given eruption, as well as the type of volcanic cone produced, depends mainly upon the proportion of each of these and the order in which they are expelled (though the kind of surrounding rock may also have some influence on an eruption).

Solid Material. The fragments of solid matter thrown out by volcanic explosions are described as *pyroclastic* (fire-broken). They may be pieces of the surrounding rock (*country rock*) or earlier deposits of the volcano itself. Some pyroclastic rocks may have cooled from a semiliquid state while whirling through the air. The term *volcanic bomb* is appropriately applied to oval-shaped pieces with twisted ends, which must once have been plastic projectiles. The other kinds of solid material are named according to their size and shape. Large angular pieces (more than 32 mm. in diameter) are *volcanic blocks;* these may weigh many tons, and may have the spongy look of pumice (solidified rock froth) as a result of the escape of gases. Pieces of intermediate size (between 32 and 4 mm.) are *cinders,* or *lapilli* (small stones). Small pieces are either *volcanic ash* (less than 4 mm.) or *volcanic dust* (less than 0.25 mm.); the finest dust may blow around in the upper atmosphere for several years before settling out. Ash compacted into rock is known as *tuff.*

Liquid Material. The liquid product of a volcano is lava; the term *lava flow* refers both to the molten matter and to the solid rock which it becomes. As the flowing lava cools, it darkens in color, and a frothy crust forms on the surface. This crust cracks into separate blocks which float in the lava as it flows along, making a *flow breccia;* some of the liquid material that fills in around the cracks may also bubble up through them and build up a small mound called a *spatter cone* on top of the crust. Rough, porous lava surfaces go under the Hawaiian name *aa,* while smooth, ropy ones are called *pahoehoe.* A pillowy surface marked by irregularly curved cracks (*pillow lava*) indicates that the lava cooled under water. Beneath the hardened crust the liquid lava may still be moving along; when it has drained away, a *lava tunnel* or *lava cave* is left.

Gas. Explosive volcanic eruptions derive their vigor from an abundance of steam and other gases. Some of this gas comes from the original magma, some from the rocks and subsurface water heated by contact with the magma, and some possibly from sea water. Besides superheated steam, the chief volcanic gas is carbon dioxide; other gases of special interest include compounds of sulfur, chlorine, fluorine, and boron. "Smoke" issuing from a volcano is really a mixture of condensing steam and dust particles. A fast-rolling incandescent cloud of superheated steam and hot ash of the sort first associated with the 1902 eruption of Mt. Pelée (Martinique) is known as a *nuée ardente,* or *fiery cloud.*

VOLCANIC CONES. A large proportion of the lava emerges from fissures in the weakened sides of a volcano rather than through the central vent, which not only is higher up but also may become choked with hardening lava. Secondary cones that develop in this way on the flanks of the main volcano are known as *parasitic cones.*

Volcanoes are classified according to the shape of their cones, which is determined by the composition and temperature (at the time of eruption) of the constituent material.

Cinder Cones. Cinder-cone volcanoes are built up of angular fragments of cinders and lapilli blown out in gas-generated explosions of considerable violence. Large pieces can stand steeply enough to make slopes of 40 degrees; finer pieces are carried downhill, so that the lower slope is more gradual.

EXAMPLE: Sunset Crater, a national monument north of Flagstaff, Arizona, is one of several hundred cinder cones in the San Francisco Mountains.

Lava Cones. A lava cone, also called a *shield volcano,* is formed by successive flows of lava, which lie on a slope rarely exceeding 10 degrees at the summit, although the angle varies somewhat with the viscosity of the flow, which is governed by the chemical composition and temperature of the flowing lava.

EXAMPLE: Mauna Loa on the island of Hawaii is one of the world's greatest shield volcanoes.

Composite Cones. A composite cone consists of alternating layers of pyroclastic material and lava, indicating cyclic changes in the nature of eruptions. This kind of cone is sometimes called a *stratovolcano* because of its layered appearance. The slope is about 30 degrees at the top and about 5 degrees at the base, where piles of blocks and bombs give way to sheets of lava.

EXAMPLE: Vesuvius is the classic example of a composite cone.

Calderas. Named for La Caldera (cauldron), a great circular pit in the Canary Islands, a caldera represents the enlargement of a normal volcanic crater as a result of the explosion or collapse of a cone. The cause of collapse may be the withdrawal of the sustaining lava column from directly beneath the cone, followed

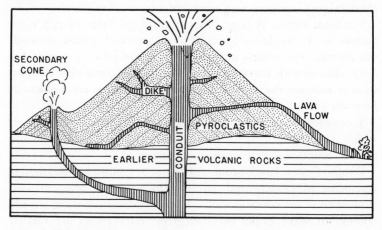

FIG. 4—Volcanic cone and associated features. (By permission from *Geology,* by von Engeln and Caster. Copyright, 1952. McGraw-Hill Book Co., Inc.)

by the subsidence of large central areas of the volcano. The width of a caldera is usually at least several times its depth; diameters of five to seven miles are not uncommon.

EXAMPLE: Crater Lake, in Oregon, is the best known example of a caldera.

DISTRIBUTION OF VOLCANOES. Volcanic activity has taken place at intervals since the beginning of geologic time, but some periods have seen a great deal more of it than others. The locations of volcanic activity have likewise shifted widely. Most vulcanism occurs within the ocean basins, a fact which is not surprising since the oceans cover about 71 per cent of the surface of the globe; and some of the earth's most massive mountains are volcanic cones rising from beneath the waters of the deep seas. The principal concentration of present-day visible volcanoes, however, is on land, along the rims of the continents, and on adjacent island archipelagoes—in long, narrow belts associated with recently formed mountain chains and daily earthquakes.

The Pacific Ocean "circle of fire" is a volcanic belt almost completely bordering that vast ocean, from the Antarctic below the tip of South America to Alaska to Kamchatka along the Siberian Coast thence south through Japan and on to New Zealand. Within the Pacific itself are numerous volcanoes situated in zones having a northwest direction. The Atlantic Ocean likewise has a long belt of volcanoes extending from West Spitsbergen in the Arctic to the Cape Verde Islands off the coast of Africa. Crossing these oceanic belts is a third one which stretches generally from the West Indies, through the Mediterranean, and on to central and southeastern Asia and the East Indies. A fourth volcanic belt runs from Palestine to Madagascar. In addition, there are a number of isolated areas of important volcanic activity.

FAMOUS ERUPTIONS. The most recent list of volcanoes that have been active within historic times numbers 476, including 60 submarine eruptions. Certain of them are so celebrated in literature, history, and geology as to be mentioned frequently in geologic textbooks. Brief summaries of important volcanoes and eruptions, stating the salient facts, are given below.

Bogoslof: In the Aleutians; submarine volcano; builds above sea level; destroys its summit by explosions; has appeared and disappeared at intervals since discovery in 1768.

Etna, Mount: In Sicily; parasitic cinder cones; frequent activity recorded since 475 B.C.; buried Catania in 1669, earliest attempt to divert a lava flow.

Graham Island: Between Sicily and Pantelleria; built 200 feet above sea level in 1831, later eroded away by waves.

Katmai, Mount: In southern Alaska; violent explosion in 1912 erupted ignimbrite (welded tuff) over large area; many resulting gas vents (fumaroles) constitute nearby Valley of Ten Thousand Smokes.

Kilauea: On southeast slope of Mauna Loa (see below); shield

volcano; large caldera with fire pit (lava lake) called Halemau-
mau; Hawaiian Volcano Observatory maintained here.

Krakatoa: Island between Java and Sumatra; cinder-cone remnant of giant prehistoric volcano; destroyed by explosions in
1883, producing noise heard 3,000 miles away, disastrous sea
waves, thick dust suspended in atmosphere for 2 years.

Lassen Peak: In California; only active volcano in conterminous
United States in historic time; eruptions at intervals since 1914.

Mauna Loa: In Hawaii; shield volcano; one of world's largest
mountains and active volcanoes.

Nuovo, Monte: Near Naples, Italy; new *(nuovo)* volcano in 1538,
active one week, built 440-foot cone; dormant since then.

Paricutin: In Mexico; cinder cone; new volcano in 1943, active
until 1952. *Jorullo,* in the same region, was born in 1759; soon
became dormant.

Pelée, Mount: On island of Martinique, West Indies; cinder
cone; explosion in 1902 destroyed St. Pierre by *nuée ardente;*
1,020-foot-high spine rose from crater. *La Soufrière,* in the same
region, erupted simultaneously.

Stromboli: One of the Lipari Islands, near Sicily; eruptions every
half hour or less; produces incandescent cloud of steam, hence
known as "lighthouse of the Mediterranean."

Tambora: On Sumbawa Island, Indonesia; enormous eruption,
1815, with sound heard 1,000 miles, 38 cubic miles of material
thrown out, great dust clouds.

Vesuvius, Mount: Near Naples, Italy; composite cone; lies within
the eroded crater of a former larger volcano called Monte Somma;
now explosive type; believed extinct until A.D. 79, when it buried
Pompeii and Herculaneum; intermittent until 1631; active since,
with recent violent eruptions in 1906, 1929, 1944.

THERMAL ACTIVITY

Under the general heading of vulcanism we must consider certain geologic activities which involve heat but are not directly concerned with magma or lava. The source of this heat lies deep

within the magma, as do the liquids and gases that produce these thermal phenomena.

The liquid phase of such activity is termed *hydrothermal;* usually the gas and liquid phases are intimately associated, but some predominantly gaseous activity occurs separately. Although water is the principal substance utilized in the formation of the coarse igneous rocks called *pegmatites,* their magmatic origin is so obvious that this material may be considered an aqueo-igneous product.

Pegmatites. As the outer portion of a large body of magma solidifies, most of the water and other volatile substances separate and become concentrated under pressure. The rock types formed in the presence of these volatiles fill open spaces formed by the shrinkage of the cooling mass of igneous rock and fractures and other openings in the surrounding country rock. The resulting extremely coarse textured rock type is called *pegmatite.* In addition to their large size and occasional rarity (some are valuable gems), the pegmatite minerals are noted for the way in which they have become intergrown (*pegma,* something fastened together). Pegmatite has been called "giant granite" because it generally consists of the same minerals as granite (chiefly feldspar, quartz, and mica), but in crystals sometimes of huge dimensions. The abundance of volatiles prolongs the period of fluidity of the magma which accounts for the size of the crystals in such rocks. A *simple pegmatite* becomes a *complex pegmatite* when gem, radioactive, and other uncommon minerals are also present. Many complex pegmatites result from the attack of hot gases and liquids on the earlier formed crystals of feldspar and other minerals of the original simple pegmatite.

Hydrothermal Phenomena. Hot water, charged with steam and other gases, escapes from congealing magma in enormous quantities, carrying with it a great deal of mineral matter which is later deposited at higher levels where the pressure and temperature are less intense. Fissures in the adjacent rock provide channelways for the movement of these solutions, and other openings also become sites where deposition takes place.

QUARTZ VEINS. Many quartz veins are deposited by solutions expelled from solidifying pegmatites and are examples of hydrothermal rocks typical of the zone adjacent to large igneous bodies, especially those of more siliceous composition. These extensive tabular or irregular bodies of quartz resist erosion and are often conspicuously exposed on the surface.

ORE VEINS. Becoming still less viscous as mineral matter crystallizes out, the hot solutions make their way upward and outward. In a rather well-defined sequence, they deposit minerals of vital importance to man's economy. An *ore* consists of useful minerals, usually intimately mixed with country rock and waste vein material called *gangue,* but sufficiently concentrated by nature so that one or more metals can be profitably extracted. The most characteristic ore deposits, called *fissure veins,* are usually found occupying cracks in the rock. These ore veins yield much of the world's gold, silver, copper, lead, zinc, and other metals.

THERMAL SPRINGS. Ore solutions that have become nearly depleted of their mineral content may deposit some of their remaining dissolved solids in open spaces other than veins. Still bearing heat from the magma, they mingle with the ordinary underground water (described in Chapter 12), and both reach the surface of the earth together as *hot, warm,* or *thermal springs.* All thermal springs are *mineral springs,* because "pure" (unmineralized) water is not found in the earth. An intermittently erupting hot spring is a *geyser.*

Gaseous Phenomena. Water vapor (steam) proves to be the main component of magmatic gas when it is analyzed at the surface. Other abundant constituents include carbon dioxide, sulfur and several of its compounds, hydrochloric acid, and ammonium chloride. The temperature of such gas may be over 650 degrees C.

FUMAROLES. A surface vent in the earth's crust from which gas of magmatic origin issues is called a *fumarole.* One that gives off gases containing considerable sulfur is a *solfatara* (It. *solfo,* sulfur). Common in regions of both active and inactive volcanism, fumaroles are used to generate power in Italy, New Zealand, Iceland, and California, and solfataras supply native sulfur in several countries.

MUD VOLCANOES. Gas that brings particles of wet clay and sand up to the surface may build a mound of mud called a *mud volcano.*

REVIEW QUESTIONS

1. What is radioactivity and what are its products?

2. What is the evidence for the existence of magma in isolated reservoirs rather than in broad zones?
3. How does magma differ in composition from the rocks that result when it cools?
4. What is the difference in composition between magma and lava?
5. How do concordant and discordant plutons differ in the field?
6. What is the difference between a batholith and a stock?
7. What are the differences between a dike, sill, and laccolith?
8. Explain the difference between a volcano and a fissure eruption.
9. How is pyroclastic material formed?
10. Define the following kinds of volcanoes: parasitic, cinder, shield, stratovolcano.
11. Locate on a world map the major volcanic belts.
12. Why do large crystals occur in pegmatites?
13. How is a fumarole related to a geyser?
14. What kind of deposition results from hydrothermal activity?

5

Geologic Structures Produced
by Diastrophism

All movements of the rocks of the earth's crust that result in permanent change are embraced by the term *diastrophism* (already defined on p. 18). As a result of diastrophism, geologic structures are produced both at and below the surface of the earth, on a large and on a small scale, rapidly and slowly. Rock may be deformed by bending or displaced by breaking.

STRUCTURES PRODUCED BY DEFORMATION

We think of the earth's crust as solid, but rocks are somewhat plastic and will bend under great pressure. When the pressure upon them exceeds their limit of elasticity, rocks become permanently bent, or deformed. Rocks buried at a considerable depth, weakened by high temperature, or subjected to long-continued stress are most likely to bend.

Warping. Slight bending on a broad scale is called *warping.* Troughs containing thick layers of sediments warp downward in the preliminary stages of mountain-building, as will be discussed later. In its broadest meaning, warping refers to wide vertical movements on a continental scale. Such *epeirogenic* (*epeiros,* mainland; *-genic,* pertaining to origin) movements can lift extensive plateaus and can restore, by isostatic compensation (see p. 23), the status of the major land masses of our globe, which otherwise would be eroded until they were permanently inundated by the sea. The ocean basins themselves doubtless participate in epeirogenic warping.

Folding. Folding is like warping except that it denotes a greater degree of deformation. Minor folds may result from the uneven settling of sediments around the crest of a hill, an effect known as *differential compaction.* Most folding, however, is due to compression caused by forces acting essentially horizontally in the earth's crust.

ELEMENTS OF FOLDS. Folds are named according to their size, shape, and *attitude* (position with respect to the directions of the compass and to the horizontal). Two key terms—*strike* and *dip*— are used to describe the geometry of attitude of inclined beds. When an inclined layer of folded rock intersects a horizontal

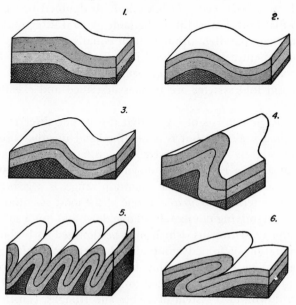

FIG. 5—Folds: (1) monocline, (2) symmetrical anticline and syncline, (3) asymmetrical anticline and syncline, (4) overturned anticline, (5) isoclinal folds, (6) recumbent fold. (By permission from *Geology Principles and Processes,* 4th ed., by Emmons, Thiel, Stauffer, and Allison. Copyright, 1955. McGraw-Hill Book Co., Inc.)

surface (land or water), the compass direction of the line formed by their intersection is called the *strike*. This term is also applied to the direction of the *axis* of a fold. Strike is given in degrees, as N 45° E, which is straight northeast. The *dip* of a fold is the acute angle between the horizontal and the axial plane, measured perpendicularly to the strike. These two factors constitute the attitude of a fold.

The sides of a fold are the *limbs*. An imaginary plane paralleling the strike and dividing the fold as symmetrically as possible is the *axial plane.* If the axis is not horizontal, we call the acute angle between it and the horizontal the *plunge,* and the fold is a *plunging fold.*

KINDS OF FOLDS. Folds may be described in the following general terms: An *open fold* is less tightly compressed than a *closed fold.* If the limbs dip at about the same angle, the fold is said to be *symmetrical;* if they dip at unlike angles, the fold is *asymmetrical.* An *overturned fold* has one limb doubled beneath the other so that both limbs dip in the same general direction; when these limbs are parallel, dipping about equally in the same direction, the structure is an *isoclinal fold;* and when the limbs are virtually horizontal, it is a *recumbent fold.*

Folds and fold systems are further described and classified as follows:

A *homocline* consists of layers that dip in one direction only. A *monocline* is similar but is a steplike bend in otherwise horizontal or slightly dipping layers. An *anticline* is a structural upfold, or arch; a *syncline* is a downfold, or trough. An arch of large size, such as an upfolded mountain range, is a *geanticline.* The opposite term, *geosyncline,* is one of the most essential words in geology, signifying not merely a large downfold but a subsiding trough and its sediments, which may be destined to become the next generation of folded mountains in that area. A large composite group of folds, including both arches and troughs but dominantly an upfolded area, is an *anticlinorium;* the reverse aspect, a downfolded system of arches and troughs, constitutes a *synclinorium.* The terms dome and basin are often applied to topographic features caused by erosion. In a structural sense, however, a *dome* is an approximately symmetrical upfold in which the strata dip outward in all directions, and a *basin* is an inverted dome in which the strata dip inward toward the center. This use of these terms carries no topographic implications.

EROSION PATTERNS OF FOLDS. The effects of erosion in folded rocks of unequal resistance are extremely complex; some of them are discussed in Chapter 11, on Streams. One curious fact is that an anticline is often eroded into a valley, while a syncline becomes the site of a hill or ridge—this is known as *inverted relief.* The erosion patterns in domes and basins are likewise interesting.

The following applies to the recognition of anticlines and synclines by means of the surface patterns they present after their interiors have been exposed by deep erosion. It is important to note that the oldest layer of rock is normally at the bottom of a pile and the youngest at the top. When cut open along the level of the ground and the "lid" removed, upright anticlines and synclines whose axes are horizontal will show nearly parallel bands of rocks. In an anticline the oldest formations are in the middle, and each bed of rocks away from the center is younger than the preceding one. Conversely, in a syncline the oldest beds are on the outside and the youngest in the middle. Plunging anticlines and synclines, having inclined axes, may be eroded in such a way that a looping ridge called a *zigzag ridge* is produced, enclosing a valley curved like the end of a canoe. The pattern of the ridge indicates the direction of plunge: an anticline plunges toward the closed end (*nose*) of the loop, and a syncline toward the open end.

EXAMPLE: Zigzag ridges caused by alternating plunging anticlines and synclines are common in the eroded Appalachian Mountains of Penn-sylvania and Virginia.

Folded Mountains. We have obtained a large part of our present knowledge about the earth from the various kinds of mountains that rise majestically above its surface. By far the most important mountain groups, both in distribution and geologic significance, are the folded ones; in fact, the term "mountain structure" is virtually confined to the deformation characteristic of the folded type. These mountains occur in systems of ranges which appear as a series of alternating ridges and valleys; their linear and arcuate forms extend far across land and sea. The arcuate character is shown strikingly by the folded ranges that extend from the East Indies north through the Philippines, Japan, and Kamchatka.

Geosynclines. All the world's major mountain ranges have risen out of deformed geosynclines, those great basins of sedimentation which originate in mobile belts along the margins of stable regions. Elongated, troughlike in form, a geosyncline accumulates an enormous amount of material derived mostly by erosion of an adjacent zone resembling an island arc, which perhaps tends to rise as the geosyncline subsides. Although the thickness of the deposits may reach a maximum of 40,000 feet, the nature of the rocks and the presence throughout them of marine-animal fossils peculiar to shallow water indicate that the depth of water in a geosyncline never exceeds 1,000 feet during the long interval of time involved. Only by slow sinking of the trough, while sediments continue to be added to it, could it maintain this relative position while the filling proceeds. This may be an intermittent process, however, with frequent interruptions and even temporary reversals, during which the surface rises above sea level for a time and is exposed to erosion.

Orogeny. As the geosyncline is depressed under the weight of 20,000 or more feet of sediments and sinks further under the influence of external forces, such as compression within the crust, the adjacent borderland not only rises (by isostasy) but also pushes over, encroaching on the trough. The bottom of the great pile of sediments gradually sinks to a considerably warmer zone. At this depth the heat makes the rock more susceptible to horizontal compression by forces within the crust and may even melt the rock, forming magma. The folding and fracturing of the rocks allows this magma to make its way upward, resulting in the intrusion of batholiths and other igneous bodies, as well as the extrusion of lava and the production of volcanoes. After most of this period of intense folding, fracturing, and vulcanism has passed, the mobile belt undergoes pronounced vertical uplift. Erosion gnaws away at the newly formed mountains, whose height is renewed by continuing uplift until equilibrium has been attained in the process of isostatic compensation. This prolonged sequence of events, greatly simplified here, is termed *orogeny,* and the mountain-forming movements belong to an *orogenic cycle.* Such mountain-building as described above has occurred about 40 times in perhaps ten distinct mountain systems since the original solidification of the earth's crust.

The source of energy and the mechanisms that cause orogeny— the gigantic lateral crushing, the fracturing and slipping, the formation of magma resulting in intrusive and extrusive vulcanism, the reversal of direction from subsidence to uplift—are among the fundamental and still largely unsolved problems of geology.

Among the numerous hypotheses that have been advanced to explain orogeny—the most significant aspect of which is crustal shortening, suggesting horizontal movement—are the following:

1. *Contraction.* This hypothesis involves the shrinking of the

earth by one or more of the following processes: (*a*) cooling; (*b*) extrusion of volcanic material from the mantle; (*c*) nuclear reactions that transform the silicate rocks of the mantle into much denser material.

2. *Convection.* This hypothesis requires the existence of convection currents in the mantle; their drag would produce large displacements of parts of the crust, either (*a*) continuously, or (*b*) intermittently.

3. *Continental Drift.* This hypothesis concerns the migration of continental bodies after their separation from the presumed one or two original continents; the front of the land mass would drag against the substratum and become folded, while island arcs would break off behind.

4. *Expansion.* The expansion hypothesis involves a yielding of the crust as a result of stresses created by expansion (perhaps by radioactivity) below it; variations include (*a*) the theory of buckling, and (*b*) the theory of rock metamorphism.

5. *Zonal Rotation.* This hypothesis depends upon different rates of rotation of the horizontal zones of the earth, increasing in velocity toward the equator.

6. *Undation.* This hypothesis assumes rhythmic oscillations of the surface, whereby material slides from high to low places, and is produced by the extension (rather than the shortening) of the original strata.

7. *Polar Wandering.* The hypothesis of polar wandering assumes changes in the position of the axis of rotation of the earth, producing crustal shortening and lengthening in different parts of the world and the shearing of the crust on a continental scale. One line of evidence for this is shown by *paleomagnetism,* whereby certain sedimentary rocks and lavas exhibit magnetic orientations presumed to show the changing direction of the earth's magnetic axis in past times. The magnetic axis may or may not coincide with the rotational axis.

STRUCTURES PRODUCED BY DISPLACEMENT

All rocks are plastic to a degree. Under directed pressure, the more plastic bend whereas the more brittle fracture. Under a light load a rock may fracture, but under a greater load it will be deformed without any tendency to rupture. The same force that opens a small fracture of no immediate moment may in time generate one of the earth's major structural features. A body of rock undergoing intense folding may give way under stress. Movement (faulting) may occur along the resulting fracture, thereby combining deformation with displacement.

Fractures. Any crack in solid rock is a *fracture*.

Fissures. An extensive fracture in rock is called a *fissure*. It may become the channelway for the passage of lava that will form plateau basalt or of ore solutions that will form ore veins.

Joints. Fractures along which no significant movement has taken place and which occur in parallel groups are called *joints*. They may originate as primary structures by the shrinkage of magma or lava when it cools to form an igneous rock (especially striking in *columnar jointing*, which yields perfectly shaped prisms of basalt) or by the shrinkage of sediments as they dry. In every kind of rock, however, joints are produced as secondary structures by the forces of *compression* (squeezing), *tension* (stretching), *torsion* (twisting), and *shear* (sliding) as the rock is subjected to later crustal movement.

A group of related more or less parallel joints (they never occur singly) is called a *joint set;* when closely spaced (a fraction of an inch apart), the effect is known as *fracture cleavage.* A set of somewhat curved horizontal joints in granite constitutes *sheet structure,* or *sheeting,* which seems due to the gradual reduction of pressure from above by erosion. Intersecting sets of joints constitute a *joint system,* the dominant set being the *master joints;* although they may meet at any angle, a nearly right-angled pattern is common. The ease of quarrying rock for construction purposes depends to a large extent upon the presence of joints, but if the joints are too close together large pieces are not attainable.

EXAMPLES: Such celebrated scenic features as the Giant's Causeway in Ireland, Devils Tower in Wyoming, and Devil Postpile in California owe their origin to excellent columnar jointing in igneous rocks.

Faults. Fractures, fissures, or joints along which appreciable slipping has taken place are called faults. The *fault surface* along which the displacement, or *faulting,* occurred is rarely flat enough to warrant the usual name *fault plane.* A *fault zone* is a zone in which a large number of faults essentially parallel are separated by disturbed or crushed rock affected by the movement. This crushed rock, along a single uneven fault surface as well as in a zone, is termed *fault breccia* (brĕch'ĭ·à) when coarse, and *gouge* or *fault gouge* when powdery and forming a claylike mass. *Fault striae* (strī'ē) are scratches or grooves on a fault surface. When friction develops between the moving blocks of rock, the fault surface becomes smooth and even highly polished, an effect known as *slickensides.*

Following old English mining terminology, we refer to the block of rock below an inclined fault as the *footwall,* because the miner would stand upon it while extracting ore from the fault surface, often a mineralized vein. The *hanging wall* would then be the block above his head.

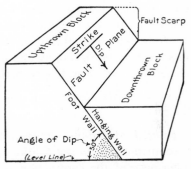

KINDS OF FAULTS. Because faults are so important in both structural and historical geology and in problems of mining and petroleum geology, a com-

FIG. 6—Elements of a fault. (By permission from Worcester, Philip G., *Textbook of Geomorphology,* 2nd ed., copyright, 1948, D. Van Nostrand Company, Inc., Princeton, New Jersey.)

plex nomenclature has developed. It is greatly simplified here. Measurements of *strike* and *dip* planes are made as with folds. The actual direction of movement along a fault is seldom known, for only the relative movement of one wall to the other can be observed. A vein or layer of rock displaced by the faulting might be bent as well as broken; such bending next to the fault is *drag* and shows the relative direction of movement. The block of rock that seems to have moved up is the *upthrown side* of the fault, while the opposite block is the *downthrown side.* Fault striae and a greater smoothness in the direction of movement are useful in determining the direction of slip.

If the hanging wall is the downthrown side, the fault is called a *normal fault* because it was once considered usual for a block of rock to drop by gravity. If the hanging wall is the upthrown side, the fault is a *reverse fault.* A low-angle reverse fault which is generated by a horizontal thrust is called a *thrust fault* or *thrust.* A *strike fault* parallels the strike of the rock layers; a *dip fault* is (like the dip of the beds itself) at right angles to the strike of the beds of rock involved. An *oblique fault* makes an angle with the directions of strike and dip of the formations. These and many other fault types may be either normal or reverse.

Fault Scarps. The surface resulting from faulting may be a low cliff on the upthrown side, especially if the displacement is rapid, and displacements of many feet may be almost instantaneous. Such a cliff is a *fault scarp*. When faulting is slow, as it usually is, erosion sometimes destroys the exposed side as soon as it appears above the other. Fault scarps, of great magnitude such as those bordering mountains, are a consequent of repeated movements over a prolonged period of time.

EXAMPLE: The abrupt east face of the Sierra Nevada is a tremendous fault scarp.

Faulted Mountains. Thrust faulting on a large scale often accompanies the intense folding in mountain ranges and provides a measure of the contraction that the earth has undergone in such regions, in some cases indicating miles of crustal shortening.

Vertical movements of enormous segments of the crust bounded by faults may produce mountains without associated folding. Many such *block mountains,* or *block-faulted mountains,* represent stationary units of the crust adjacent to blocks that have been pulled away and dropped down.

EXAMPLE: Numerous isolated mountain ranges in the Basin and Range province of the western United States (Utah, Nevada, Arizona) are block mountains.

A single elongated block raised between two normal faults is called a *horst*. A trenchlike block lowered between two normal faults is a *graben*.

EXAMPLE: The Rhine Valley depression of Alsace between the mountainous Black Forest area in Germany and the Vosges Mountains in France is the classic example of a down-dropped block or graben between two tiled blocks, which are not horsts, since these higher masses are not bounded on both sides by faults. The elevated Vosges and the Black Forest areas are the limbs of a great arch, the down-dropped keystone of which is the Alsatian lowland.

EROSION ALONG FAULTS. Streams often follow fault zones where these reach the surface, and a line of springs may mark the trend of the fault. Erosion eventually may reverse the topography, causing the originally higher upthrown side of a fault scarp to wear away faster and become the lower side. Escarpments whose location is determined by faulting but whose present form is a consequence of erosion are called *fault line scarps.*

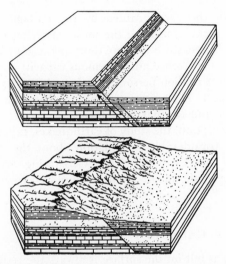

Fig. 7—Erosion of a fault scarp (above) into a fault-line scarp (below). (By permission from *Geology: Principles and Processes,* 4th ed., by Emmons, Allison, Stauffer, and Thiel. Copyright, 1955. McGraw-Hill Book Co., Inc.)

REVIEW QUESTIONS

1. Why can rocks bend?
2. Draw a fold and mark the limbs, axial plane, and axis.
3. Sketch an anticline, syncline, and monocline.
4. What does the nose of an anticline indicate as to direction of plunge?
5. Discuss the role of geosynclines in orogeny.
6. Outline the sequence of events in a typical orogenic cycle.
7. Account for the jointing in granite. What is columnar jointing?
8. What evidence of faulting might be observed in the field?
9. Distinguish a horst from a graben.

6
Earthquakes

Tremors in the earth, caused by the passage of vibrations through the rocks, constitute the most terrifying of all natural phenomena, feared since ancient times because of their sudden, unpredictable occurrence and enormous capacity for destruction. An estimated 13 million persons have been killed by earthquakes during the past 4,000 years, including more than 2 million persons in ten quakes that have taken place since 1,000 A.D. In partial compensation, the study of earthquakes, called *seismology*, has given us considerable information about the structure and properties of the earth's interior. Generating artificial earthquakes is one of the major methods employed in the search for petroleum.

CAUSES OF EARTHQUAKES

The quake as felt on the surface is always the result, never the cause, of some more fundamental geologic process. The geologic effects, in turn, are relatively slight, even though they may seem impressive by human standards. Perceptible but local and unimportant earth tremors may be caused in many ways, both natural and man produced, such as by an avalanche, rockfall, or landslide; an explosion; or the passage of heavy traffic. The slumping of submarine sediments, the collapse of a cavern roof, and especially the eruption of a volcano are among the likely causes of such weak shaking within shallow levels of the earth's crust. It has not been determined how much influence is exerted by isostatic adjustment to imbalance resulting from the overloading of a delta or the upwarping of land after glaciers have retreated.

The really significant earthquakes are all of *tectonic*, or structural, origin, being due to movements within the solid earth, and specifically to faulting associated with mountain building. This is true even when accompanied by a volcanic explosion, and even when no displacement can be discerned at the surface.

52

The *elastic-rebound theory* (developed to interpret the San Francisco disaster of 1906) explains the characteristic association of earthquakes with faulting. Regardless of their intensity or the depth at which they originate, or whether the faults are horizontal, vertical, or inclined, the wave patterns of earthquakes are basically alike. As stresses (forces) accumulate in the rock on both sides of a fault, the rock is pressed tightly together and slowly distorted until its elastic limit is reached. Then the rock ruptures suddenly and releases its stored-up energy in earthquake waves as it snaps back (rebounds) into positions approximating its earlier unstrained condition. *Foreshocks* and particularly *aftershocks* are part of the normal earthquake pattern.

DEPTH OF ORIGIN

The source of the waves initiated by a given act of faulting is called the *focus,* and it is generally an area of limited extent along the fault. The place on the ground directly above the focus is the *epicenter*.

Earthquakes are classified according to the computed depth of the focus, as follows:

1. *Shallow quakes,* the most numerous, originate within 37 miles (60 kilometers) of the surface, always within the crust of the earth; most of them begin less than 5 miles (7 kilometers) down.

2. *Intermediate quakes* start from 43 to 186 miles (70 to 300 kilometers) down.

3. *Deep quakes* begin below 186 miles (300 kilometers) and are known as far down as 447 miles (720 kilometers). At such depths the viscosity of the mantle is sufficient to allow large stresses to build up temporarily, although the rock tends in the long run to yield slowly by a sort of plastic flow. All but a very few of the deep quakes are confined to the margins of the Pacific Ocean Basin.

These arbitrary depths, which are identified by the particular wave pattern that arises, have not yet been correlated with the zonal structure of the earth, to which they ought in some way to correspond. The maximum energy released by earthquakes becomes less as the focus becomes deeper, indicating a decline in breaking strength of the rock.

KINDS OF EARTHQUAKE WAVES

The energy released by an earthquake moves in the form of waves through the rock, which acts as an elastic body. The individual particles in the rock vibrate rapidly to and fro as they transmit the wave motion. There are a number of kinds of seismic waves. Their patterns become extremely complex when modified by the wave properties of reflection, diffraction, refraction, and dispersion. The three main types of earthquake waves are described below.

P Waves. Also called the *primary, push, compressional,* or *longitudinal wave,* the P wave is a fast *body wave* that travels through the interior of the earth and arrives first at the recording station. It is transmitted (like sound waves) by alternate compression and expansion of the volume of the rock along the direction in which the wave travels. This kind of wave can go through solid, liquid, or gas; in solid rock it generally has greater velocity at greater depth, where the rock is more elastic. For this reason it can travel faster through ocean basins than through continental masses, and faster through the mantle (except in the Gutenberg low-velocity zone) than through the crust. The speed of the P wave is 3.7–7.0 miles (6.0–11.3 kilometers) per second.

S Waves. Also called the *secondary, shake, shear, distortional,* or *transverse wave,* the S wave is a slower body wave than the P wave. Likewise traveling through the interior of the earth, it is the second to arrive at the recording station. It is transmitted (like light waves) by vibrations at right angles to the path that the wave travels in the rock. The velocity of this kind of wave is proportional to the rigidity of the material through which it passes, and it cannot go through liquid; hence the inference previously stated (see p. 24) regarding the differing nature of the earth's core and the mantle. The S wave has a speed of 2.2–4.5 miles (3.5–7.3 kilometers) per second.

L Waves. Also called *long,* or *surface, waves,* these are slow, undulating waves that go just beneath the surface of the earth. Two main kinds are known: *Love waves* in uniform solids, and *Raleigh waves* in non-uniform solids. Even when not felt upon the ground, this type of wave may have enough energy to go more than once around the earth. The velocity of the L wave is 2.2 miles (3.5 kilometers) per second, varying with the elasticity of the rock.

SEISMOGRAPHS AND SEISMOGRAMS

A *seismograph* is an instrument that records earthquakes. It operates on the principle that a heavy metal weight suspended from a supporting post by a wire or by a coiled spring will remain at rest, due to inertia, while the bedrock beneath it vibrates rapidly in an earthquake. The supporting post is firmly attached to a concrete base which is anchored to solid rock, so that it moves only when seismic waves pass through that spot. The difference in displacement between the post and the stationary heavy weight reveals the amount of horizontal ground motion; and that between the post and the stationary spring reveals the amount of vertical motion. To register all components of horizontal movement, two units must be set at right angles to each other, and a third one is needed for the vertical component. Many varieties of seismographs are in use, ranging in size from huge ones weighing tons and kept in subterranean vaults to those that fit the hand and are valuable in prospecting for minerals.

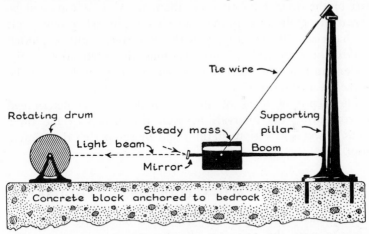

FIG. 8—Seismograph of horizontal pendulum type. (By permission from *Principles of Geology*, 2nd ed., by J. Gilluly, A. C. Waters, and A. O. Woodford. San Francisco and London: W. H. Freeman and Company, 1959.)

The recording device of a seismograph may employ mechanical or optical means, if necessary magnified electromagnetically or electronically, to transfer the tremors onto a permanent record called a *seismogram*. An inked pen may trace its zigzag mark on a strip of paper wound on a revolving drum driven by a synchronized motor; a sharp stylus may scratch the record on smoked or chemically treated paper; or, more usually, a tiny beam of light may be reflected by a mirror onto photographic paper. The vibrations must be magnified (usually between 100 and 100,000 times) in order to be recorded at an appreciable distance from the epicenter of the quake, and they must always be accurately timed.

It is important to time the movement of the seismograph with precision because the relative time of arrival of the three chief kinds of earthquake waves indicates the distance at which they originated. The first evidence that a shock has occurred is a series of short wiggles on the recording device; these indicate the passage of the P waves. The slower S waves then begin to be recorded as a series of larger zigzags. From the time lag between the arrival of the P and S segments, the distance from the focus to the instrument station can be calculated. A later, more pronounced set of zigzag lines indicates that the L waves are being received.

Finding the distance to the source of an earthquake gives only part of the desired information about it. A circle can then be drawn on a globe or map; the quake has originated at some point on that circle. If such a circle with the correct radius is plotted at three or more widely spaced stations, the intersection of the circles must be the epicenter. Other methods of locating the quake are used for special cases.

The depth of focus of an earthquake can be determined by comparing the intervals between the arrival of the three kinds of waves at various stations and by comparing their intensities.

INTENSITY AND MAGNITUDE OF EARTHQUAKES

No quantitative method is available for measuring earthquake *intensity* near the epicenter. Earthquake intensity is usually measured in a qualitative way by estimating its visible geologic effects and the destruction of life and property. These effects differ from place to place, and contour lines called *isoseismal lines* are drawn on a map to separate the zones of different degrees of shaking. The area of maximum destruction is within the central contour, surrounded by elliptical zones of decreasing damage. The scale most commonly used to measure the intensity of quakes is the Modified Mercalli by Wood and Neumann. It comprises grades of intensity or destructiveness from I (not directly felt) to XII (nearly complete wreckage of most man-made structures).

The usefulness of such scales is limited because the amount of damage varies from spot to spot, owing to the differing factors involved, and because personal opinions enter too much into their preparation. Seismologists have consequently devised a scale independent of human estimates of damage. It is based upon the *magnitude* of the effect of earthquake waves on a standard Wood-Anderson seismograph situated at a definite distance (62 miles, or 100 kilometers) from the epicenter. Specifically, it is computed from the measurement of the maximum amplitude of the horizontal trace on the seismogram. For other distances and other instruments it is necessary to calculate the magnitude. The Richter scale is the one most commonly used today. On it the smallest recorded quake is zero and the largest known is about 9.0. This magnitude expresses fairly accurately the total energy released by the earthquake at its source; the energy increases tenfold for each higher number. Statistics of earthquake occurrence reveal that most of the total energy of a quake is concentrated in a relatively small number of very large shocks.

EFFECTS OF EARTHQUAKES

The effects of earthquakes range from the frightful to the grotesque. The destructiveness of a quake is determined by such factors as the velocity, acceleration, period, and duration of the earthquake waves; the geologic nature of the rock and soil; and the size, shape, material, design, and quality of construction of buildings and other structures. Fire, fanned by wind and impossible to control because of broken water mains, is the most serious hazard in cities subjected to earthquakes.

Geologic Effects. Numerous changes take place in the topography as a consequence of the more severe earthquakes. Of minor importance as geologic agents, earthquakes may nevertheless be disastrous to people affected by them. Fissures often open in the ground, although stories about many persons being swallowed up in them are untrue. Ridges may form by compression at right angles to the cracks. The circulation of underground water is disturbed, interfering with the functioning of wells, springs, and geysers. Lakes may be set in rocking motion. The displaced earth, previously assumed to be *terra firma,* sinks in some places and rises in others; the change in level is most conspicuous along the shore of the ocean, where beaches are lifted above sea level or depressed and inundated. Landslides occur frequently in hilly regions, and avalanches occur in rugged snow-covered country. Glaciers are affected in several ways, and icebergs are set loose from the ends of glaciers that have reached the sea.

Tsunamis. Among the most spectacular of the natural effects of earthquakes are the seismic sea waves called *tsunamis* (Japanese) and popularly known as "tidal waves" though they have nothing to do with tides. Generated by earthquakes, almost always of submarine origin, they pile up repeatedly on the shore, creating great devastation. They may sweep at speeds exceeding 600 miles per hour across the ocean as long, low waves which may attain a height of 100 feet as they approach shallow water.

DISTRIBUTION AND PREDICTION OF EARTHQUAKES

The zones of major seismic activity in the earth correspond closely to those of volcanism (see p. 37), and both are associated with belts of young mountains.

Earthquake Zones. Surrounding the ancient shield areas of the continents (see p. 16) and the large stable block of the Pacific Ocean Basin (excluding the vicinity of the Hawaiian Islands) are situated the following main earthquake zones:

1. The borders of the Pacific Ocean, with many complex branches, including a branching loop through the Caribbean Sea, the islands of which are structurally like the circumpacific belt. In this belt occur about 80 per cent of all shallow quakes, 90 per cent of the intermediate ones, and 99 per cent of the deep ones. The largest of the intermediate and deep quakes are assigned to Japan. More deep quakes take place in the triangle of the Fiji, Tonga, and Kermadec Islands than anywhere else.

2. The Mediterranean—trans-Asiatic (so-called Alpide) belt, merging with the arc that runs through the East Indies. Here occur all the rest of the intermediate and many of the remaining large shallow quakes.

3. The Pamir—Baikal belt of central Asia. It is noted for large shallow quakes.

4. The Mid-Atlantic Ridge, extending into the Arctic Ocean, and a similar branching belt in the Indian Ocean. Here occur numerous shallow quakes.

5. The Hawaiian Islands, the rift valleys of eastern Africa, and a broad triangular area in eastern Asia.

Frequency of Earthquakes. It is estimated that about one million true earthquakes happen each year. Perhaps 150,000 of them are strong enough to be felt by persons nearby, and 100 are severe enough to be fairly destructive.

Predicting Earthquakes. Attempts to correlate the occurrence of earthquakes with sun spots or other astronomical data, tides, or the weather have not been successful, though there may be some relationship. No regular cycle is known.

Protection from Earthquakes. A good deal has been learned about the kinds of structures that minimize earthquake damage. Buildings can better withstand the trembling of the earth if they are erected upon bedrock, are reinforced to move as a unit, and have low centers of gravity and light roofs and chimneys.

FAMOUS EARTHQUAKES

The following list includes some of the outstanding earthquakes of recorded history, with brief notes on the casualties and special features of geologic interest. They are given in chronologic order because the names of the localities may differ and the relative intensity is known only for those of the twentieth century.

1456	Naples, Italy: 60,000 dead.
1556	Shensi Province, China: 830,000 dead (largest loss of life in history).
1693	Catania, Sicily: 60,000 dead.
1731	Peking, China: 100,000 dead.
1737	Calcutta, India: 300,000 dead.
1755	Lisbon, Portugal: Perhaps strongest quake in history; seismic sea waves; rocked Loch Lomond, Scotland; aftershocks continued several months; 60,000 dead; first scientific study.
1811–1812	New Madrid, Missouri: Thousands of shocks, some felt over most of United States; land thrown into waves;

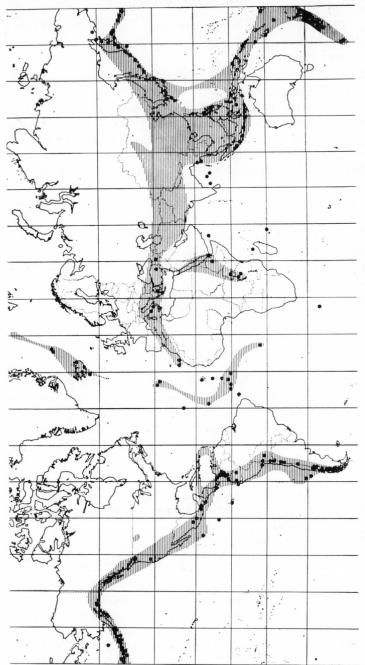

Fig. 9—World distribution of major earthquake belts (shaded) and volcanoes (dots).

created Reelfoot Lake, Tennessee; changed topography and land boundaries.

1868   Chile and Ecuador: Tsunami carried several large ships inland.

1886   Charleston, South Carolina: Felt over eastern United States; aftershocks continued more than a year.

1897   Assam, India: Very severe; land thrown into visible waves; scarp raised 35 feet; almost complete destruction of buildings over 30,000 square miles; aftershocks continued 2 years.

1899   Yakutat Bay, Alaska: Seacoast uplifted more than 47 feet; glaciers affected.

1906   Chile: Very severe.

1906   Colombia and Ecuador: Very severe.

1906   San Francisco, California: Horizontal movement along San Andreas fault; very severe quake and devastating fire; later study led to elastic-rebound theory.

1908   Messina, Sicily: Coast depressed several feet; tsunamis; 75,000 dead.

1911   Tien Shan Mountains, Asia: Very severe.

1920   Kansu Province, China: 180,000 dead, most buried in landslides of loess.

1922   Chile: Very severe; great tsunamis in Pacific.

1923   Kwantō Province, Japan: Yokohama and Tokyo destroyed; tsunamis; extensive fires; 143,000 dead.

1927   Kansu Province, China: Repetition of 1920 disaster.

1929   Grand Banks of Newfoundland: Submarine slides; transatlantic cables broken; 50-foot tsunamis.

1933   Long Beach, California: Locally severe; considerable damage.

1939   Turkey: 23,000 dead.

1950   Tibet and Assam, India: Very severe; landslides and floods.

1952   Kern County, California: Extensive damage.

1959   Hebgen Lake, Montana: Landslide; new lake formed; damage in Yellowstone Park.

1960   Agadir, Morocco: 12,000 dead; city destroyed.

1960   Chile: Widespread; 5,000 dead; large tsunami damage in Hawaii and Japan; first detection of earth's free oscillation.

1962   Iran: 12,225 dead.

1963   Skoplje, Yugoslavia: city destroyed.

1964   Alaska: Very severe; widespread damage and tsunamis.

REVIEW QUESTIONS

1. What is the major cause of all large earthquakes?
2. What are other natural causes of the earth's trembling?
3. Explain the elastic-rebound theory.
4. How are earthquake depths classified?
5. What is the pattern of movement in each of the three main types of earthquake waves?
6. How does a seismograph operate?
7. How does a seismograph record the distance at which earthquakes originate?
8. How is the epicenter of an earthquake determined?
9. What is the difference between earthquake intensity and magnitude, and how are they derived?
10. What are tsunamis and why are they so destructive?
11. Locate on a world map the major earthquake belts.

7
Minerals

The known rocks of the earth's crust are composed mainly of minerals. A knowledge of the chief rock-forming minerals is therefore essential to the study of rocks. Important minerals constitute the ore bodies, which yield metals; others make up the commercial deposits of nonmetallic minerals; and still others, though of no economic value, are widely distributed through the earth.

A *mineral* is a homogeneous substance that has a definite chemical composition (and can be represented by a chemical formula) and an orderly geometric arrangement of atoms (*crystal structure*); it has been produced by natural inorganic processes. The orderly internal structure of minerals is often expressed in outward geometric form, providing us with the symmetrical objects to which the term *crystal* is applied. Being homogeneous, a mineral exhibits uniformity and constancy in its *properties,* which are the qualities and characteristics by which it may be recognized and identified. These properties may be chemical or physical (including optical).

CHEMICAL COMPOSITION OF MINERALS

Some minerals consist of only one of the 92 naturally occurring chemical *elements,** which may be a metal (such as copper or sulfur) or a *nonmetal* (such as carbon, which is found as graphite and as diamond). Most minerals, however, consist of two or more elements united in a *compound* (such as quartz, the chemical name of which is silicon dioxide, SiO_2).

The chemical *formula* of a compound gives its composition by means of a shorthand notation in which each element is represented by a *symbol* (an abbreviation of either the English or the Latin name of the element) and numerals indicate the propor-

* Eleven elements not occurring in nature have been created in the laboratory (1967).

tions in which each element is present. Thus the formula SiO_2 means that quartz consists of an arrangement of silicon and oxygen atoms in the ratio of 1:2.

An *atom* is a minute system in some ways like the solar system, with negatively charged particles called *electrons* revolving very rapidly around a *nucleus,* which, in turn, contains positively charged *protons* and uncharged *neutrons,* as well as a number of other particles not named here. The *atomic number* of an element is the number of protons in the nucleus. (Since an oxygen atom has eight protons, its atomic number is 8.) The sum of the weights of the protons and neutrons in the nucleus gives the *atomic weight* of the element (common carbon is the standard, with an atomic weight of 12).

When an atom loses or gains electrons and becomes electrically unbalanced, so as to carry a positive or negative charge, it is spoken of as an *ion;* positive and negative ions attract each other and unite to become solid matter. Most minerals are composed of such ions spread throughout the entire structure to form a *crystal lattice.*

More than 99 per cent of the earth's crust is composed of nine elements; the following list names the 15 most abundant elements.

	Per Cent		Per Cent
Oxygen (O)	46.60	Titanium (Ti)	.44
Silicon (Si)	27.72	Hydrogen (H)	.14
Aluminum (Al)	8.13	Phosphorus (P)	.12
Iron (Fe)	5.00	Manganese (Mn)	.10
Calcium (Ca)	3.63	Sulfur (S)	.05
Sodium (Na)	2.83	Carbon (C)	.03
Potassium (K)	2.59	Chlorine (Cl)	.03
Magnesium (Mg)	2.09	All others, total	.50

CRYSTALS

The atoms or ions in all true minerals are arranged in a symmetrical three-dimensional pattern (the crystal lattice) and are said to be *crystalline.* The few exceptions, sometimes called *mineraloids,* have their atoms distributed at random and are therefore *amorphous* (shapeless). Under favorable conditions most crystalline minerals grow as crystals, which are solid bodies having smooth plane surfaces (*faces*) oriented in accordance with their internal structure. Hence the angle between corresponding faces of any given mineral always remains the same, regardless of the size or mode of origin of the specimen. All similar faces on a crystal constitute a *form*. For example, some varieties of the mineral garnet crystallize into structures with twelve like faces—crystals known as dodecahedrons. Crystals occur in a great variety of forms, and a knowledge of these forms is useful in the identification of minerals.

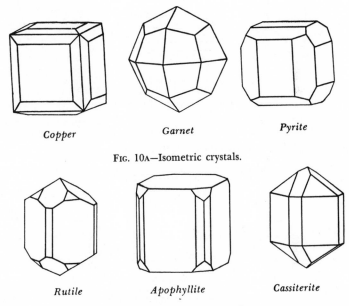

Copper	Garnet	Pyrite

FIG. 10A—Isometric crystals.

Rutile	Apophyllite	Cassiterite

FIG. 10B—Tetragonal crystals.

No matter how varied they may be, all crystals—artificial as well as natural, organic as well as mineral—can be classified into six main divisions called *crystal systems*, which are based upon the number, position, and relative lengths of the axes of the crystals. (The *axis* of a three-dimensional geometric figure is an imaginary line extending through the center of the figure.)

1. *Isometric* crystals have three mutually perpendicular axes of equal length.

2. *Tetragonal* crystals have three mutually perpendicular

axes; the two horizontal axes have equal lengths and are either longer or shorter than the vertical axis.

3. *Hexagonal* crystals have four axes: the three horizontal axes have equal lengths and intersect at angles of 120 degrees; the vertical axis is at right angles to and is either longer or shorter than the horizontal axes.

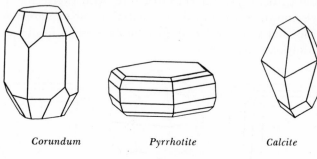

| Corundum | Pyrrhotite | Calcite |

Fig. 11—Hexagonal crystals.

4. *Orthorhombic* crystals have three mutually perpendicular axes, each having a different length.

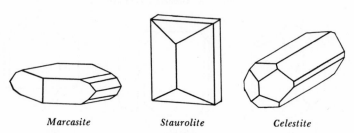

| Marcasite | Staurolite | Celestite |

Fig. 12—Orthorhombic crystals.

5. *Monoclinic* crystals have three axes, each having a different length; two of them meet in the center at right angles, and the other is inclined forward and downward.

6. *Triclinic* crystals have three axes, which meet in the center at oblique angles and have different lengths.

Crystals of any of these six systems may occur in irregular groups or as *twin crystals*. *Twins* are groups of two or more crystals united at some specific angle. In some cases a crystal of one mineral may change into another of the same chemical composition by a re-arrangement of the atoms taking place in the

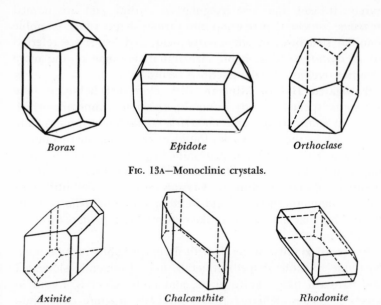

Borax *Epidote* *Orthoclase*

FIG. 13A—Monoclinic crystals.

Axinite *Chalcanthite* *Rhodonite*

FIG. 13B—Triclinic crystals. (Crystal drawings reproduced from *Rocks and Minerals*, by Richard M. Pearl, copyright, 1956, Barnes & Noble, Inc.)

solid state. When this occurs the external shape of the crystal does not change. An example is the orthorhombic mineral aragonite $CaCO_3$, which changes rather readily into the hexagonal form of $CaCO_3$ called calcite. A crystal of one mineral can also be chemically changed into another by loss or addition of certain elements. In this case the original external form is also retained. A good example is pyrite, FeS_2, which on weathering may lose its sulfur and take on oxygen and water, being thereby converted into the hydrous iron oxide mineral called limonite or goethite, which is often found in the shape of a pyrite crystal.

HABITS OF MINERALS

The crystal form or combination of forms that a mineral typically develops in response to heat, pressure, and other factors in the geologic environment is called its *habit*. Some minerals always develop particular crystalline forms; others, even when they possess a regular atomic structure, develop well-formed crystals only rarely. Instead, they are irregular in outline and are termed *massive;* or else they develop into various shapes which resemble familiar structures in our environment, and hence are referred to as *imitative.* Most habits are imitative; some of the more familiar ones are briefly described below.

Elongated Habits. Minerals with elongated habits include *prismatic* (pencil-shaped) minerals; *columnar* minerals, which occur in stout pillars; and *stalactitic* (*stalaktos,* dripping) minerals, such as the stone icicles found in caves. Thinner examples include *acicular* (needle-shaped) minerals; *fibrous* minerals, growing in silky threads; *capillary* (hairlike) minerals; and *filiform* (twisted and matted) minerals. Crystals radiating in all directions from a common center are said to be *radiating* or *stellated* (starlike); those that show a latticelike network are *reticulated* (*reticulum,* net).

Flattened Habits. Minerals with flattened habits include *tabular* (table- or tablet-shaped) minerals; *bladed* minerals, elongated and flattened like a knife blade; and *platy* minerals, found in sheets or plates. *Foliated* (leafy) minerals separate easily into leaves or scales, and *micaceous* minerals do so to an extreme degree. *Dendritic* (branching) or *arborescent* (treelike) minerals branch out like ferns or ice crystals on an icy windowpane.

Rounded Habits. Minerals with rounded habits include small spheres which resemble fish eggs and are called *oölitic* (*oö-,* egg) or if larger *pisolitic;* aggregates of globules of an appropriate size are *botryoidal* (like a cluster of grapes); larger rounded masses are *reniform* (kidney-shaped); still larger ones are *mammillary* (breastlike). Concentric groupings of platy crystals are *rosettes.* Surfaces that are covered with a myriad of closely set tiny crystals are known as *drusy.*

PHYSICAL PROPERTIES OF MINERALS

The properties, or characteristics, by which a mineral can be identified are numerous, ranging from simple and obvious ones, such as color, to those that can be detected only by elaborate equipment, such as an electron microscope. The physical properties most useful to the student of minerals in elementary geology are described below.*

* Other properties, the chemical composition, origin, and occurrence of the most important and interesting members of the mineral kingdom are described in *Rocks and Minerals,* by Richard M. Pearl, published by Barnes and Noble, Inc., 1956.

Structures. The term *structure* or mode of aggregation refers to gross structure, the way in which groups of crystals or mineral grains are intergrown. The descriptive terms applied to the outward form are the self-explanatory terms: *granular, compact,* and *earthy.*

Color. Some minerals have a constant color or gradation of colors (sometimes in zones) which aids greatly in recognizing them. Other minerals vary in color from one specimen to another, owing to the presence of impurities, a change in chemical composition, or structural alterations due to radioactivity, and their recognition is difficult. Certain metallic minerals *tarnish,* so that only a fresh surface will reveal the true color.

Streak. When crushed to powder, most minerals turn white or become a paler tint of their ordinary color. A few show a color in powdered form that is different from their color in larger fragments and may be distinctive enough to help in identifying them. The same effect is produced by rubbing the specimen on a piece of unglazed porcelain known as a *streak plate,* and the resulting color is called the *streak* of the mineral.

Luster. The nature of the light reflected from the surface of a mineral is its *luster.* Determinative mineralogy generally begins by separating minerals into two groups, those having a *metallic luster* and those having a *nonmetallic luster.* Some minerals have a *submetallic luster,* with not quite the appearance of a typical metal.

The nonmetallic lusters are classified according to familiar substances which they may resemble. A *pearly* luster has the iridescence of pearl and is commonly shown by minerals with a platy structure and is often seen on cleavage surfaces of minerals (see "Cleavage," below). A *greasy* luster looks oily. A *silky* luster results from a fibrous habit. A *resinous* luster is that of yellow resin (it is not implied that the mineral has the color of resin). *Vitreous* (glassy) is the luster of minerals that look like glass. An *adamantine* (diamondlike) luster is very brilliant.

Hardness. The hardness of a mineral (written H) is determined by its ability to scratch or be scratched by others in the scale of hardness, called *Mohs' scale* after the mineralogist who proposed it more than a century ago. This scale is given below:

1 Talc	3 Calcite	5 Apatite	7 Quartz	9 Corundum
2 Gypsum	4 Fluorite	6 Orthoclase	8 Topaz	10 Diamond

For the sake of comparison, a few common objects have been given ratings:

> 2½ Fingernail (which will scratch gypsum)
> 3 Copper cent
> Slightly over 3: Brass pin (which can scratch calcite)
> 5½ Window glass
> 6 Knife blade of good-quality steel
> 6½ Hardened-steel file

In making the hardness test, care should be taken to differentiate between an actual scratch made by a harder substance and a temporary powdery mark left by a softer one. When the mineral is loosely held together—splintery, for instance—or has an altered surface, this test may not be reliable.

Cleavage. When minerals tend to break in definite directions along planes of weakness in their crystal lattice, yielding smooth plane surfaces, they are said to have *cleavage*. Each cleavage is parallel to two possible crystal faces, and minerals may have one, two, three, four, or six directions of cleavage. This feature is a valuable aid to identification, even when observed only as small cracks beneath the surface. Cleavage is described by telling (1) how easily it is produced; (2) what crystallographic direction it has—i.e., in what direction it tends to break; and (3) the number of directions in which it occurs in the crystal. A cleavage plane can generally be distinguished from a crystal face by its pearly luster.

Fracture. When a mineral has no cleavage it breaks irregularly with a *fracture*. The most conspicuous kind of fracture is called *conchoidal* (shell-like) because it shows concentric arcs like the inner surface of a clam shell. Glass breaks with this type of fracture. A *hackly* fracture has jagged edges, as formed on broken metal. More ordinary kinds of fracture are called *even* if fairly smooth; or *uneven* or *irregular* if rough; or *fibrous* or *splintery* if like wood; or *earthy*.

Tenacity. Most minerals are brittle; they crack or powder readily. This is true no matter how hard they may be in resisting scratching or how tough they may be in resisting cleaving or fracturing. A few minerals are *sectile* (cuttable) and can be cut into shavings with a knife. Some can be pounded into a thin plate and so are called *malleable;* most such minerals are also *ductile* and so can be drawn out into wire. Certain minerals are *flexible;* others are *elastic.*

Specific Gravity. The relative weight of a mineral, compared to water as a standard, is termed its *specific gravity* (**G.** or **S.G.**). Thus, a mineral that weighs exactly three times as much as the same volume of water has a specific gravity of 3.00. The specific gravity of the most familiar nonmetallic minerals in the earth's crust falls between 2.50 and 3.00; when a nonmetallic mineral is heavier or lighter than this common range, even a small difference will be noticed by anyone who handles minerals frequently. Many of the common metallic minerals have a specific gravity over 5, and again one who is familiar with minerals will note the unusual weight of a metallic mineral with a different specific gravity. Mineralogists use a Jolly balance, beam balance, pycnometer, or heavy liquids to determine specific gravity; but after a little practice the student can become adept at estimating the approximate values by hefting specimens in his hand.

Magnetism. A small number of minerals are sufficiently magnetic to be attracted by an ordinary pocket magnet, and this property serves as a means of identifying them.

ROCK-FORMING MINERALS

All the minerals of the earth's crust occur in and among the rocks, for they are an integral part of the rocks. Of the nearly 2,000 different minerals that are known, however, only a few, referred to as the *rock-forming,* or *rock-making, minerals,* are the essential constituents of the common rocks described in Chapter 8. Concise descriptions of these minerals are given below, in an order corresponding to the arrangement of rocks in Chapter 8.

The streak is white and the minerals are brittle unless it is otherwise stated; where no fracture is mentioned, cleavage is assumed to be the chief manner of breaking.

Feldspar Group. A group of minerals constituting almost half the earth's crust, the feldspars are aluminum silicates of two principal kinds:

(1) *Potash,* or *potash-soda, feldspar,* usually called *orthoclase,* though it is often *microcline.* Formula: $KAlSi_3O_8$. Pink or gray; pearly or vitreous luster; H 6; two cleavages at right angles; S.G. 2.56.

(2) *Soda-lime feldspar,* known as *plagioclase,* which is arbitrar-
ily divided into six subspecies, of which only the dark *labradorite*
(often showing a play of colors) and *albite* (in the platy variety
called cleavelandite) have a distinctive appearance. Plagioclase is
generally recognized by the fine *striations* (parallel lines) on a
cleavage surface which is due to twinning. Formula: $NaAlSi_3O_8$
(albite) to $CaAl_2Si_2O_8$ (anorthite). The various members of the
plagioclase series are isomorphous mixtures of these two "end
members." White to dark gray; pearly to vitreous luster; H 6.0–
6.5; two cleavages almost at right angles; S.G. 2.59–2.76.

Quartz. Gray or colorless grains of quartz are very common in
many kinds of rocks; tapering six-sided crystals of quartz form in
cavities. Formula: SiO_2. Colorless, white, and various hues; vitreous to greasy luster; H 7; conchoidal fracture; S.G. 2.56.

Courtesy of Ward's Natural Science Establishment

Fig. 14—Quartz crystals: Hot Springs, Arkansas.

A different type of quartz without crystal form (actually crypto-crystalline or microcrystalline) and with a slightly lower hardness (6.0–6.5) and specific gravity (2.60) is known as *chalcedony;* this includes varieties that are very important in certain rocks and go under the names *flint, chert,* and *jasper.*

Pyroxene Group. The most frequent member of the pyroxene group to be seen in rocks is *augite,* which occurs in stubby crystals and irregular masses; other members include *enstatite, hypersthene,* and *diopside.* Composition: complex silicates containing calcium, magnesium, aluminum, iron, sodium. Dark green or black; dull to vitreous luster; H 5–6; two cleavages nearly at right angles; S.G. 3.1–3.6.

Amphibole Group. Resembling pyroxene though generally having a brighter luster, longer crystals, and a different cleavage, the amphibole group has *hornblende* as its most familiar member. Composition: complex hydrous silicates of calcium, magnesium, iron, and aluminum. Green to black; vitreous luster; H 5–6; two cleavages at oblique angles; S.G. 2.9–3.8.

Mica Group. The most common members of the mica group are muscovite and biotite; both are noted for their extraordinary cleavage into elastic sheets. They are common rock-forming minerals:

(1) *Muscovite,* or white mica. Composition: hydrous potassium aluminum silicate. Colorless to green; pearly luster; H 2.0–2.5; S.G. 2.7–3.0.

(2) *Biotite,* or black mica. Composition: hydrous potassium iron and magnesium aluminum silicate. Dark brown to black; pearly luster; H 2.5–3.0; S.G. 2.8–3.2.

Olivine. Sugary grains of olivine, whether isolated or in massive form, are an important constituent of many rocks. Formula: $(Mg,Fe)_2SiO_4$. Olive green to yellowish green; vitreous luster; H 6.5–7.0; uneven fracture; S.G. 3.2–3.5.

Kaolinite. Ordinary clay consists of a number of related soil-forming minerals, of which kaolinite is the best known by name. It feels greasy and is plastic when wet. Composition: complex hydrous aluminum silicate. White; dull luster; H 1.0–2.5; earthy fracture; S.G. 2.6.

Calcite. A widespread mineral occurring in granular or cleavable masses, calcite grows in cavities as tapering crystals called "dog tooth spar." Being a carbonate, it will fizz or *effervesce* in dilute acid. Formula: $CaCO_3$. Colorless, white, and various hues; dull to pearly luster; H 3; cleaves obliquely into rhombs (i.e., in three directions); S.G. 2.7.

Dolomite. Similar to calcite but effervescing less readily unless powdered, dolomite is found in granular masses and also often shows curved crystal faces. Formula: $CaMg(CO_3)_2$. White, gray, pink; vitreous to pearly luster; H 3.5–4.0; rhombohedral cleavage (i.e., in three directions); S.G. 2.8.

Gypsum. Occurring in several habits, including the fibrous satin spar, compact alabaster, and crystalline selenite, gypsum is an abundant product of evaporation. Formula: $CaSO_4 \cdot 2H_2O$. White; vitreous to pearly luster; H 2; one perfect cleavage; S.G. 2.3.

Anhydrite. Closely related to gypsum, anhydrite is an abundant mineral in many places, occurring in masses of varying degrees of coarseness. Formula: $CaSO_4$. White; vitreous to pearly luster; H 3.0–3.5; blocky cleavage in three directions at right angles, which distinguishes it from calcite and dolomite; S.G. 2.9–3.0.

Halite. The mineral name for common, or rock, salt is halite; its taste is a distinctive property. Granular masses and cubic crystals are common. Formula: NaCl. Colorless or white; vitreous luster; H 2.5; cubic cleavage in three directions at right angles; S.G. 2.1.

Chlorite. Resembling green mica but flexible instead of elastic, chlorite is a group of minerals including *clinchlore, penninite,* and *prochlorite,* which develop in platy masses. Composition: complex hydrous magnesium iron aluminum silicate. Green; greasy to vitreous luster; H 2.0–2.5; cleaves into flakes, often curved; S.G. 2.65–2.96.

Serpentine. Usually a smooth, massive mineral having a greasy feel. A variety of serpentine called chrysotile is the most important kind of *asbestos.* Composition: hydrous magnesium silicate. Green; greasy luster; H 4; uneven fracture; S.G. 2.5–2.8.

ORE MINERALS

As stated previously (see p. 63), an *ore* is a rock or mineral deposit from which a metal may be extracted on a commercial basis. Several hundred minerals, yielding one or more metals each, are mined throughout the world. Of this number, perhaps a dozen are of such great importance as to be studied in the usual course in beginning geology. These are described briefly below.

Magnetite. The richest ore of iron, magnetite is named from its property of being attracted by a magnet. Octahedral crystals are fairly common, but this mineral usually forms granular masses. Formula: Fe_3O_4. Black; black streak; metallic luster; H 6; even fracture; S.G. 5.2.

Hematite. The most abundant ore of iron, hematite is the cause of most of the red color in rocks. It often occurs in massive or oölitic form, but it may be granular, fibrous, micaceous, or earthy. Formula: Fe_2O_3. Reddish brown to gray; reddish-brown streak; metallic luster; H 5.5–6.5; uneven fracture; S.G. 4.9–5.3.

Limonite. This is a general name for all hydrous oxides of iron, both crystalline and amorphous. It is an ore of iron. Crystalline hydrous oxide of iron is correctly known as *goethite*. Earthy and compact masses of limonite, often with rounded and stalactitic habits are of widespread occurrence; disseminated limonite imparts brown, orange, and yellow colors to soils and rocks. Composition: hydrous iron oxide. Yellowish to dark brown; yellowish-brown streak; metallic or earthy luster; H 5.5; uneven fracture; S.G. 3.3–4.3.

Pyrite. Exceedingly common in striated (lined) crystals and granular masses, pyrite ("fool's gold") is often an ore of copper and gold, which are present as chemical impurities. Formula: FeS_2. Brass yellow; black streak; metallic luster; H 6.0–6.5; uneven fracture; S.G. 5.0–5.1.

Chalcopyrite. The most important ore of copper and often an ore of gold or silver, massive chalcopyrite is another mineral referred to by prospectors as "fool's gold." Formula: $CuFeS_2$. Brassy; greenish-black streak; metallic luster; H 3.5; uneven fracture; S.G. 4.1–4.3.

Galena. The major ore of lead, galena is also often an ore of silver, which it contains as an impurity. Cubic crystals and granular masses are common in association with various zinc minerals. Formula: PbS. Lead gray; same color streak; metallic luster; H 2.5; cubic cleavage in three directions at right angles; S.G. 7.4–7.6.

Sphalerite. Granular masses of sphalerite constitute the principal ore of zinc, though crystals are not uncommon. Formula: ZnS. Yellow brown to dark brown; white to brown streak; resinous luster; H 3.5–4.0; cleavage in six directions; S.G. 3.9–4.2.

Cassiterite. Almost the sole ore of tin, cassiterite occurs in tetragonal pyramidal crystals and rounded pebbles. Formula: SnO_2. Brown to black; white to pale-brown streak; adamantine to metallic luster; H 6–7; uneven fracture; S.G. 7.0.

Bauxite. Although known to be a mixture of several hydrous aluminum oxide minerals (gibbsite, boehmite, diaspore), in addition to an amorphous constituent (called cliachite), bauxite is usually regarded as an ore mineral or material and is the only commercial source of aluminum. Its pisolitic structure renders its identification easy. White, gray, and brown; white streak; earthy luster; H 1–3; uneven fracture; S.G. 2.0–2.6.

Uraninite. The most valuable ore of uranium. It is called *pitchblende* when impure and found in rounded masses. It alters to a wide range of colorful secondary uranium minerals, mostly yellow, orange, or green, of which the yellow *carnotite* is best known. Formula: UO_2. Black with a black streak; pitchy luster; H 5–6; conchoidal fracture; S.G. 6.5–10.0.

NONMETALLIC MINERAL RESOURCES

Hundreds of nonmetallic minerals find their way into industry, where they serve a great variety of uses in a technological society. They run the gamut from energy-producing fuels to gem stones for adornment, from constructional materials to fertilizers, from heavy chemicals to abrasives, from pigments to constituents of food.

The nonmetallic mineral resources that are generally given attention in an elementary course in geology are coal and petroleum (and natural gas). These are not actual minerals since they do not have definite chemical compositions that can be expressed by a chemical formula. Because they come from the earth, however, they are referred to as *mineral resources*. They are often called *fossil fuels* because the energy that they release has been stored in the rocks for long geologic ages.

Coal. Coal is a rock of organic origin; it is derived from plant life which was once lush vegetation in coastal swamps. The dead plants, when partially decomposed by microorganisms, were buried by other sediments which protected them from complete destruction. As the volatile constituents were driven off, the carbon became concentrated, and the plant accumulations passed successively through the stages of peat, lignite (brown coal), bituminous (soft coal), anthracite (hard coal), and eventually to graphite, if the geologic conditions favored so complete a transformation.

Petroleum. Oil and gas occur together in a complex mixture of gaseous, liquid, and solid hydrocarbons. Doubtless they also originated together, although there is no certain knowledge as to their source. Most geologists believe that they are derived from the bodies of marine organisms that accumulated in stagnant water on the bottom of shallow seas, where they were decomposed by bacteria, leaving residual carbon and hydrogen. Further chemical changes resulted from burial by sediments, which finally squeezed the oil and gas into porous rocks beneath, from which they eventually migrated to suitable reservoir rocks.

REVIEW QUESTIONS

1. Define a mineral.
2. Name the eight most abundant elements in the earth's crust.
3. How is the atomic weight of an element computed?
4. Identify these parts of an atom: nucleus, proton, electron.
5. What is a crystal lattice?
6. Name the six crystal systems and describe their axes as to number, relative lengths, and angular relationships.
7. Describe these mineral habits: acicular, micaceous, botryoidal.
8. What is the streak of a mineral?
9. Give Mohs' scale of hardness.
10. How does cleavage differ from fracture?

8
Rocks

Rocks are the essential building materials of which the earth is constructed. The architecture of our planet results from the kinds of rocks that are present, the positions or attitudes they assume, and the processes acting upon them.

The geologist's definition of *rock* is broader than that of everyday language. Ice and even water may be considered by the geologist as rocks. The engineering geologist regards loose superficial material, whether soil or sediment, as rock because it has been derived from once compact material. The intimate mixtures of minerals characteristic of ore deposits form another type of rock.

Most rocks are aggregates of two or more individual minerals (see definition of *mineral* on page 63). The preponderance of the earth's crust, however, consists of only the 25 minerals—out of almost 2,000 known species—which are to any extent abundant.

The geologic significance of a rock specimen lies in the faithfulness with which it represents the larger body from which it came.

KINDS OF ROCK BODIES

According to the basic nature of their mineral content, rocks fall into four different categories, as follows:

1. *Monomineralic rocks,* consisting essentially of a single mineral, which occurs on a large enough scale so that it can be considered an integral part of the structure of the earth. Other minerals may be incorporated as impurities, though many such rocks are remarkably simple in their uniformity. Some limestones and marbles belong in this category.

2. *Natural glass,* often nearly homogeneous but not having a composition that can be expressed by a chemical formula, because it varies from place to place in the same mass.

3. *Organic matter,* an animal or vegetable product.

4. *An aggregate of two or more minerals,* with or without a

78

groundmass of natural glass. Many such rocks contain a dozen different minerals, mostly observable only under high magnification. The great majority of rocks belong to this group.

TYPES OF ROCKS

All rocks may be divided into three large groups based on their modes of origin. Certain members of each of these groups grade into one another (unlike minerals rocks are not classified by sharp boundaries). But, in general, practically all rocks can be classified without difficulty, as follows:

1. *Igneous rocks,* formed by the solidification of cooling molten material, as discussed in Chapter 4.

2. *Sedimentary rocks,* including rocks formed at the surface of the earth from accumulations of mud, sand, and gravel derived from the weathering and transport of pre-existing rocks (cemented together by deposits of mineral matter once held in solution in underground water). Other sedimentary rocks, such as limestone and gypsum, consist almost entirely of material deposited from solution.

3. *Metamorphic rocks,* formed at depth, under great heat and pressure, by the alteration of either igneous or sedimentary rock.

The one conspicuous exception to this classification is granite, which seems to originate both from a molten state and by the transformation of sedimentary rocks under conditions of extreme metamorphism. This latter process, called *granitization,* is now an accepted mechanism for producing granite, but its quantitative importance in nature is not known and is still a subject of heated debate among geologists.

In the field, rocks are classified *megascopically,* by examining them in the outcrop or in the hand. In the laboratory a much more elaborate classification is possible because *thin sections* (slices of rock ground to a standard thickness of nearly .03 millimeter, mounted on a glass slide and protected by a cover glass) can be examined *microscopically*. In the study of elementary geology, a modified field classification is used for examination of rocks because it requires only a hand lens, a bottle of acid to test the carbonate content, a streak plate, a magnet, and a knife blade or glass plate to identify the minerals by their most easily determined properties. Characteristic specimens of all the impor-

tant kinds of rocks should be studied and, if possible, compared
with their occurrence in the field.

IGNEOUS ROCKS

Table 2 gives a simplified classification of igneous rocks applicable to sight identification of hand specimens. Igneous rocks are
classified on a twofold basis: (1) chemical (mineral) and (2) tex-
tural. Texture refers to size, shape, and pattern of the mineral
grains, and is indicated by the position of the rock name in the
vertical columns. The position of a rock in the horizontal row
indicates its chemical or mineral composition (its position in the
sequence commonly referred to as acid to basic).

Texture. The igneous rocks, both intrusive and extrusive, have
different textures which usually indicate the condition under
which they cooled. Although the chemical composition of the
magma plays a part, the size of the mineral grains depends chiefly
on the rate of cooling, as determined by temperature and pressure
and the presence of volatiles. Coarse interlocking textures (called
phaneritic, granitoid, or *granitic*) result from slow cooling, aided
greatly by large amounts of water and other volatile substances.
Fine textures (called *aphanitic* or *felsitic* if the grains are indis-
tinguishable) result from rapid cooling, which indeed may take
place so fast that only a *glass* is formed. Mixed textures (called
porphyritic) are generally explained as representing two stages of
solidification; they consist of larger crystals called *phenocrysts*
embedded in a *groundmass* of finer aphanitic crystals which
solidified about the phenocrysts. Broken igneous rocks, shattered
by volcanic explosions and reassembled afterward, have a *fragmental,* or *pyroclastic,* texture.

Mineral Content. The kinds and amounts of the various minerals in an igneous rock depend principally on the chemical composition of the magma or lava. *Acidic rocks* (also called *silicic*
or *persilicic rocks*) have a high content of silica; quartz and feldspar predominate in them, and they are typically light in color
and low in specific gravity. Examples are granite and rhyolite.
Basic rocks (subsilicic rocks) have a lower content of silica but
more iron and magnesium, which yield *ferromagnesian* (also
called *mafic* or *femag*) minerals, such as pyroxene, amphibole,
biotite, and olivine. These minerals make basic rocks darker and

TABLE 2
CLASSIFICATION OF IGNEOUS ROCKS

Main Classes of Rocks According to Texture	Subdivisions of Main Classes—According to Mineral Content							
	Light-colored Minerals, Chiefly Feldspars, Predominate						Dark Minerals Predominate	Dark Minerals Only
	More potash than plagioclase feldspar		Potash and plagioclase feldspars about equal		More plagioclase than potash feldspar			
	Quartz	Quartz under 5%	Quartz	Quartz under 5%	Quartz	Quartz under 5%		
Coarse-Grained Phaneritic (granitoid, granitic) (may be porphyritic)	Granite	Syenite (Nepheline syenite, with nepheline in addition to feldspar)	Quartz Monzonite Granodiorite	Monzonite	Quartz diorite (Tonalite)	Diorite	Gabbro Dolerite (Diabase) (medium texture)	Dunite (olivine) Peridotite (olivine, pyroxene) Pyroxenite (pyroxene)
Fine-Grained Aphanitic (Felsitic) (often porphyritic)	Rhyolite	Trachyte (Phonolite, with nepheline in addition to feldspar)	Quartz Latite	Latite	Dacite	Andesite	Basalt	
Glassy (may be porphyritic)	Obsidian (vitreous luster) Pitchstone (pitchy luster) Perlite (pearly luster) Pumice (vesicular structure)	Based on chemical composition; minerals tiny or absent					Basaltic glass (Tachylyte) Scoria (cellular)	
Fragmental (pyroclastic)	Tuff (fine), Volcanic breccia (coarse)							

heavier, even though some feldspar is frequently present. Examples are gabbro, dolerite, and basalt. Extremely basic rocks, with almost no feldspar, are known as *ultrabasic*. Examples are dunite, peridotite, and pyroxenite.

The distinction between acidic and basic rocks is arbitrary, since there is complete gradation from one extreme to the other. It is therefore convenient to consider a group of *intermediate rocks* which lie between acidic and basic rocks in composition.

Kinds of Igneous Rocks. Brief descriptions of the main igneous rocks are given below, with emphasis on those included in Table 2.

GRANITE. *Granitic rocks* include true granite and other rocks, commonly called "granite," to which different names more properly apply; much of the granite used in buildings and monuments is of the latter class.

The essential minerals necessary to the classification of true granite are potash feldspar and quartz. Plagioclase feldspar and biotite mica or amphibole (hornblende) are usually present. Many granites contain scattered grains of muscovite mica, as well as minor *accessory minerals* (such as magnetite, apatite, and zircon) which do not influence the naming of the rock. The color of granite—white, gray, pink, or red—is largely determined by the color of the feldspar.

Exceptionally large amounts of certain minerals give rise to varieties such as biotite granite, hornblende granite, and so forth. When some of the minerals grow to abnormal sizes, the rock is known as *pegmatite,* described on page 39; other kinds of igneous rocks sometimes possess a pegmatitic mixture. Rock of a uniformly fine-grained texture and granitic composition is referred to as *aplite.*

SYENITE. Similar in texture to granite, but with less silica and little or no quartz is syenite; it is much less common than granite. The other minerals are rather similar to those in granite. *Nepheline syenite* is an important though uncommon rock containing, in addition to feldspar, the mineral nepheline, which belongs to the *feldspathoid group* of minerals.

MONZONITE. A granitoid intrusive in which both potash and plagioclase feldspar are present in about equal proportions (they have somewhat different colors), is called *monzonite.* The dark minerals are mainly biotite mica, amphibole (hornblende), and pyroxene (augite). If quartz is also present, as in granite, the rock is *quartz monzonite* or *granodiorite* (the difference between them is a technical one, based upon the ratio of potash to plagioclase feldspar).

DIORITE. Plagioclase is the dominant feldspar in diorite, another intrusive igneous rock less common than granite. Diorite contains abundant dark minerals, resembling monzonite in this respect. When quartz is present, the rock is termed *quartz diorite* or *tonalite*.

FELSITE. The acidic and intermediate igneous rocks that are so fine-grained that the minerals can scarcely be recognized without a microscope are grouped together under the name *felsite*. Banding due to the flow of congealing lava, inclusions, and gas cavities (*vesicles*) are common features of felsites. Each of the main types of felsite (which is of extrusive origin) corresponds in quantity and kind of feldspar to an intrusive rock of similar chemical composition. However, the minerals in felsite may differ in some respects and certain minerals are apt to stand out as they do in porphyries.

Rhyolite is the extrusive equivalent of granite; its most prominent grains are quartz, though potash feldspar and biotite mica are common. *Trachyte* is the equivalent of syenite. *Phonolite* (with nepheline) is the equivalent of nepheline syenite, and often emits a ringing sound when struck. *Latite* is the equivalent of monzonite, and *quartz latite* of quartz monzonite or granodiorite. *Andesite,* the equivalent of diorite, shows mostly feldspar grains. *Dacite* is the equivalent of quartz diorite. Rhyolite and andesite are very abundant and are found in various colors. Rhyolite is usually buff, cream, or purplish; andesite is darker, often gray or greenish.

GABBRO. Its chief minerals are pyroxene (augite) and plagioclase feldspar (usually *labradorite*). Gabbro may also contain hornblende and olivine and is a typical basic igneous rock. An important variety of gabbro consisting almost exclusively of labradorite is called *anorthosite;* another kind containing hypersthene (a pyroxene) is named *norite. Dolerite* or *diabase* is a medium-grained gabbro.

PERIDOTITE. The intrusive igneous rock consisting principally of olivine and pyroxene is named *peridotite*. When the rock consists almost entirely of olivine, it is *dunite;* when pyroxene is the

sole essential mineral, it is *pyroxenite*. A special variety of peridotite is the diamond-bearing *kimberlite* of South Africa and Arkansas. These rocks often contain, or are associated with, the heavy
metals such as nickel, chromium, and platinum. Extrusive equivalents are extremely rare.

BASALT. The aphanitic equivalent of gabbro is basalt, the most
abundant of all lavas. Its vesicles when filled by minerals such as
quartz or calcite are known as *amygdales*. Basalt and similar
dark, fine-grained igneous rocks often go under the field name of
traprock.

PORPHYRY. An appreciable number of phenocrysts in the
groundmass (see page 80) makes any igneous rock a *porphyry*.
Thus, among those described above are granite porphyry, syenite
porphyry, monzonite porphyry, diorite porphyry, felsite porphyry,
basalt porphyry, and related rocks. Many of the ordinary aphanitic rocks, no matter what name they bear, tend generally to be
porphyritic.

OBSIDIAN. The glassy equivalent of the acidic and intermediate
rocks is called *obsidian*. In spite of its dark color (usually black,
but sometimes gray, brown, or red), obsidian is not a basic rock.
When magnified, obsidian shows incipient crystallization which
accounts for the dark color.

If appreciable water is present, natural glass is called *pitch-
stone* or *perlite,* according to the luster. Frothy glass, consisting
of winding tubes filled with air so that it floats on water, is
pumice.

The basic equivalent of obsidian is known as *basaltic glass* or
tachylyte; the corresponding cellular rock is *scoria*.

PYROCLASTIC ROCKS. Volcanic ash from an eruption becomes
tuff when consolidated; some becomes welded tuff when fused
together in a fiery cloud of hot gases. Coarser fragments produce
volcanic breccia, which may be of either explosive or flow origin.

SEDIMENTARY ROCKS

Sedimentary rocks are composed of material ultimately derived
from the disintegration, by weathering and erosion, of older
igneous, sedimentary, or metamorphic rocks. Sedimentary material falls into two categories: (1) dissolved mineral matter
which is precipitated by inorganic or organic agents and (2)

solid fragments, or sediment, which accumulates to become a body of rock. Dissolved mineral matter forms the precipitated sedimentary rocks, and the solid fragments accumulate to form the fragmental or clastic sedimentary rocks. The precipitated mineral matter also contributes to the cementation of the clastic material. These sedimentary materials become compact rocks by the following processes:

1. *Compaction*, whereby water is squeezed out (most sediments are deposited in water, though some are carried by the wind or ice) and the individual particles are pressed together by the weight of the overlying sediments. Older sediments are usually more closely consolidated than younger ones, because they are apt to have been more deeply buried or subjected to earth movements, but degree of compaction is no proof of age.

2. *Cementation*, whereby the mineral matter held in solution by underground water is deposited between the grains to bind them together. The many substances cementing sedimentary rocks include calcium carbonate (calcareous cement) and silica (siliceous cement), as well as lesser amounts of iron oxide (ferruginous cement), clay, and gypsum.

3. *Recrystallization*, which enables small grains to grow into larger and stronger ones, or new minerals to form in the open spaces between others. *Replacement* may later substitute new and more stable minerals for earlier formed ones.

4. *Chemical alterations*, including reduction, especially of iron compounds by organic matter; destructive distillation of organic matter; and the activities of bacteria and bottom-dwelling animals.

Fragmental Rocks. Sedimentary rocks composed of particles of sediment from a previous source constitute the group known as the *fragmental, clastic, detrital* (from *detritus,* debris), or *mechanical* rocks. The loose material is classified on the basis of the size of the fragments as in the following modified Wentworth scale:

	Name	*Diameter in Millimeters*
	Boulder	larger than 256
Gravel	Cobble	64 to 256
	Pebble	2 to 64
	Sand	$\frac{1}{16}$ to 2
Mud	Silt	$\frac{1}{256}$ to $\frac{1}{16}$
	Clay size	smaller than $\frac{1}{256}$

Sediment may also be classified according to the agent of deposition (e.g., wind-blown dune sand), but unfortunately the geologic history is not always known.

The name of the resulting sedimentary rock corresponds not only to the size of the fragments but also to their *texture* (shape and arrangement) and to the composition of both grains and cement. Besides the actual name of the sedimentary rock, a combination of terms may be needed to describe it adequately according to its various aspects. Table 3 gives a highly simplified classifi-

TABLE 3
CLASSIFICATION OF SEDIMENTARY ROCKS

Classified by Composition	Rock	Classified by Origin	Rock
I. Clastic Sediments			
A. Coarse or mixed particles			
1. Rounded	Conglomerate		
2. Angular	Breccia	Glacial deposit	Tillite
		Hillslope weathering	Talus breccia
3. Shells	Coquina		
B. Medium to small particles			
1. Chiefly quartz	Sandstone		
2. Much feldspar as well as quartz	Arkose		
3. Shells	Limestone		
C. Indistinguishable particles			
1. Fine quartz sand	Siltstone	Wind deposit	Loess
2. Mud (very fine quartz and clay)	Mudstone & Shale		
3. Clay	Shale & Marl		
II. Nonclastic Sediments			
Calcium carbonate	Limestone	Spring carbonate deposit	Travertine
Calcium magnesium carbonate	Dolomite	Hot-spring silica deposit	Geyserite
Silica	Chert & Diatomite		
Vegetable carbon	Coal		
Salt	Rock salt		
Calcium sulfate	Anhydrite		
Hydrous calcium sulfate	Gypsum		
Phosphate	Phosphate rock		

cation of sedimentary rocks suitable for laboratory and field use. Typical rock specimens should be studied indoors and out, to learn more about the variations which exist in nature.

Precipitated Rocks. Mineral matter that is dissolved in water may be removed from it in two principal ways:

1. By inorganic chemical processes, becoming a *chemical* (or *inorganic*) *precipitate.* Among the solutions leached from the

land that are particularly abundant are sodium chloride, calcium sulfate, silica, carbonates of calcium and magnesium, and compounds of phosphorus, barium, manganese, and iron.

2. By the action of plants and animals, becoming an *organic* (or *biogenic*) *precipitate.* Living things extract such chemicals as silica, calcium carbonate, and phosphates from fresh and sea water for the development of their supporting and protective hard structures such as bones, shells, and teeth. Other organisms cause chemical reactions to occur in what seems to be the ordinary way of inorganic processes. It is often extremely difficult to determine in which manner a given sedimentary rock was actually created.

Kinds of Sedimentary Rocks. Mixtures of clastic and nonclastic sedimentary rocks are very common, for the precipitated matter that serves as a cement assumes an increasing proportion of the total volume of a normally fragmented rock. Even an organically produced rock can be broken up and its pieces recemented together as fragments.

Brief descriptions of the main sedimentary rocks are given below, with emphasis on those included in Table 3.

CONGLOMERATE. Cemented gravel is termed *conglomerate.* Any kind of rock material may constitute the fragments, but quartz and chalcedony are especially abundant. The size of the pieces may vary widely, and usually sand grains fill the interstices. Glacial deposits form rough, coarse conglomerates called *tillites.* When the gravel is relatively unworn rubble, with sharp edges and pointed corners, the rock is called a *sedimentary breccia.* *Rudite* is a general term for conglomerate and breccia.

SANDSTONE. Grains the size of sand become lithified to sandstone or *arenite.* Quartz is the typical mineral, making a *quartzose sandstone,* but interesting sandstones may be composed largely of gypsum or coral. Heavy placer minerals such as magnetite, rutile, and zircon may be sufficiently abundant to produce so-called black sands or yellow sands. *Placer minerals* are those very resistant to weathering and heavy, which therefore become concentrated in running water or along beaches. Gold placers are produced in this way. *Greensand* or *glauconitic sandstone* contains a high percentage of the mineral glauconite. (The color of sandstone is usually, however, determined by the nature of the

Pan American Petroleum Corp.

FIG. 15—Sedimentary strata. Uintah Basin, Utah.

cement—red, brown, and green being due to the presence of iron.) *Arkose* is a variety of sandstone in which feldspar is prominent in addition to quartz. *Graywacke* is a sandstone consisting largely of dark rock fragments, usually slates or fine-grained basic igneous rock. *Calcarenite* consists of sand-sized grains of calcite and hence is a detrital limestone.

SHALE. The most frequently occurring sedimentary rock on all the continents is shale, composed of mud (silt and clay), the finest particles of sediments. Hence it appears homogeneous to the eye, though mica and quartz are generally present to some extent. Sandy shales are termed *arenaceous;* organic matter makes a black, *carbonaceous* shale. *Calcilutite* consists of mud-sized grains of calcite.

LIMESTONE. Of the dominantly nonclastic sedimentary rocks, limestone is the most common. Some limestone has undoubtedly been formed by direct chemical precipitation, but most has evidently been built up in large part by the accumulation of shells and skeletons of organisms which remove calcium carbonate from sea water in order to make their resistant parts. The open spaces are then filled by deposits of the same material crushed to powder by the waves or precipitated from the water. Calcite, the chief mineral component of limestone, effervesces in acid.

Chalk is a soft, porous limestone. *Coquina* is a limestone consisting largely of shell fragments that are clearly visible. *Marl* is a very fine-grained limy material often mixed with clay (the word has other meanings, especially among foreign geologists).

DOLOMITE. Resembling limestone in most ways, dolomite (or dolostone) is formed when magnesium replaces part of the calcium in limestone. The mineral dolomite is somewhat harder, heavier, and less soluble in acid than calcite; it effervesces in cold acid only when scratched or powdered.

GYPSUM. Thick beds of the mineral gypsum constitute one of the common sedimentary rocks, which goes by the same name, and is interlayered with other sedimentary rocks that also are produced by the evaporation of sea water.

ANHYDRITE. Composed of the mineral anhydrite, the rock of this name can change to gypsum in the presence of moisture, and the reverse change can take place when gypsum is heated or strongly compressed to drive off its water content.

ROCK SALT. The enormous quantity of halite (rock salt) dissolved in the oceans is ample to explain the thick layers of this material that have been deposited throughout geologic history. When reasonably pure, this rock is easy to identify by its taste.

Other *evaporites* occur in various parts of the earth and may be commercially valuable. Among the useful evaporites are potash salts, nitrates, phosphates, and borates.

COAL. Coal is regarded as a sedimentary rock because it is found in layers. However, it originated neither as fragments nor by chemical precipitation. Its geologic story, from plant life to graphite, is briefly summarized on p. 76.

METAMORPHIC ROCKS

Igneous and sedimentary rocks can, under suitable conditions, be materially changed, without melting, into the third great group, the metamorphic rocks. The transformation, or *metamorphism,* is the result of a changed geologic environment, in which the stability of the rocks can be maintained only by a corresponding change in their make-up. Metamorphism is characterized by the development of new textures, new minerals, or both, and these are often so unlike the former ones that it is frequently difficult to determine the nature of the original rock. Table 4 gives a simplified classification of metamorphic rocks.

New textures are produced by *recrystallization,* whereby the minerals grow into larger crystals having a different orientation. A characteristic structure of metamorphic rocks is *foliated* (leaf-like), wavy, or banded due to a parallel arrangement of platy or elongated minerals. Such rocks tend to separate along the foliation as *rock cleavage.*

New minerals are created by *recombination;* the chemical constituents form new partnerships, in which minor impurities take on a more significant role. Although there are a considerable number of minerals of strictly metamorphic origin, most metamorphic rocks are similar in composition to the rocks from which they were derived.

Factors in Metamorphism. The rather drastic changes involved in metamorphism are the effects of heat, pressure, and fluids, usually acting together. Heat from within the earth and molten bodies of rock, as well as from pressure and friction, speeds up chemical activity. Pressure may come about by simple burial, but movements of the crust are more effective in altering textures. Water and gas supply the mobility for the required changes to take place, and they may carry elements from a nearby magma to facilitate the chemical changes.

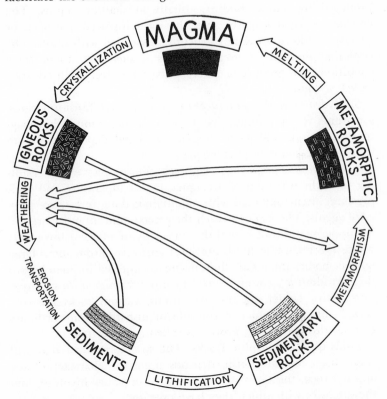

Fig. 16.—The rock cycle. Interior arrows show possible interruptions of cycle. (L. Don Leet & Sheldon Judson, *Physical Geology*, copyright 1954 by Prentice-Hall, Inc., Englewood Cliffs, New Jersey. Reproduced by permission of the publisher.)

Kinds of Metamorphism. According to the factors involved, four types of metamorphism may be distinguished, although, as is true of virtually all geologic processes, they merge and interact with one another.

1. *Geothermal metamorphism* results from the deep burial of

rocks, such as that which occurs when sediments are buried in a geosyncline (see p. 44). The pressure of overlying material, together with the heat thereby generated, produces a transformation of the rock.

2. *Dynamic,* or *kinetic, metamorphism* refers to the changes produced by crustal folding, usually at shallow depths. The crushing force frequently gives the rocks involved a broken or *cataclastic* (down-breaking) structure, associated with faults. The confining pressure at greater depths is sufficient, under these conditions, to produce a finely pulverized, recrystallized rock called *mylonite.*

3. *Hydrothermal metamorphism* covers the transformations, sometimes very profound, that accompany the action of hot magmatic solutions and gases. *Replacement* and deposition of ore minerals are common phenomena.

4. *Contact metamorphism* embraces the complex effects resulting from the intrusion of a magma; high temperature and high pressure, often combined with mountain-making forces, are powerful agents. These effects reach their maximum intensity around the upper margins of batholiths, especially in adjacent limestone, where the intruding fluids are most corrosive. From some large igneous bodies the highly fluid magma is injected intimately into the surrounding "country rock" to produce *migmatite* or *injection gneiss.* Under extreme conditions, various rocks are converted into a product hardly distinguishable from ordinary granite; this converting process is called *granitization.*

Kinds of Metamorphic Rocks. The specific product that will result from metamorphism depends upon the character of the original rock, the types of metamorphic processes involved, and the intensity with which they have operated.

Gneiss. The most coarsely banded metamorphic rock is *gneiss,* usually consisting of alternating bands or lenses of unlike appearance. Bands rich in feldspar and quartz (the dominant constituents of most gneiss) are more granular and lighter in color than those rich in biotite mica, hornblende (amphibole), or garnet.

Schist. When the platy or micaceous constituents dominate, gneiss grades into *schist.* The visible minerals, moreover, are likely to be much more uniform in appearance and composition, having little feldspar, and adjacent layers generally consist of the same minerals. The extreme foliation of schist causes it to split readily so that this kind of separation is known as *schistosity*. On the basis of the most prominent mineral present, the varieties called mica schist, hornblende or amphibole schist, and chlorite schist, etc., are recognized.

PHYLLITE. *Phyllite* is intermediate in texture between schist and slate, and tends to break into slabs, the surfaces of which show minute crumpling.

SLATE. A uniformly fine-grained rock, *slate* splits easily into smooth, lustrous plates (*slaty cleavage*). It often contains black carbon in the form of graphite, as well as iron and manganese minerals, which give it various colors such as red or green.

MARBLE. The metamorphism of either limestone or dolomite produces the massive (nonfoliated) crystalline rock called *marble*. Impurities tend to be segregated into knots or spread out in the striking patterns so familiar in this rock. The principal minerals are calcite or dolomite.

QUARTZITE. Sandstone thoroughly altered by metamorphism becomes *quartzite*. It has a glassy appearance on a fractured surface, and the fractures pass indiscriminately through the grains and the cement around them.

Other metamorphic rocks consisting almost exclusively of a single mineral include *serpentine* (composed of the mineral of the same name), *soapstone* (mostly talc), and *amphibolite* (mostly hornblende).

TABLE 4

CLASSIFICATION OF METAMORPHIC ROCKS

Mineral Composition and Structure	*Rock Name*
PARALLEL STRUCTURE:	
Coarse texture—feldspar, quartz, other silicate minerals, chiefly mica and amphibole	Gneiss
Coarse texture—mica and other platy or elongated silicates with minor amounts of quartz and feldspar	Schist
Intermediate texture—micaceous rock representing a transition from schist to slate	Phyllite
Very fine texture—micaceous minerals with quartz, other impurities	Slate
MASSIVE STRUCTURE:	
Feldspar and other silicates	Granulite
Quartz grains and quartz cement	Quartzite
Calcite or dolomite	Marble
Serpentine	Serpentine
Talc	Soapstone
Hornblende	Amphibolite
Clay	Hornfels
Pyroxene and garnet	Eclogite

REVIEW QUESTIONS

1. What is the geologist's definition of a rock?
2. Why is each of the following regarded as a rock: rock salt, obsidian, coal, granite?
3. Name the three main types of rocks.
4. Why must a field classification of rocks be simpler than a laboratory classification?
5. What determines the texture of igneous rocks? Describe the following: granular, aphanitic, porphyritic.
6. How are typical acidic rocks distinguished from basic rocks?
7. Describe the processes by which sediments become compact rocks.
8. In what two ways are sedimentary rocks formed?
9. What factors cause the metamorphism of rocks?
10. How is contact metamorphism produced?

9
Weathering and Soils

When exposed to the atmosphere, rocks slowly break down. This breaking down, termed *weathering,* is occasioned by contact of the rock with water, air, and organisms; they create soil, as well as prepare the rocks for their eventual removal by the agents of *erosion* discussed in subsequent chapters. Weathering and erosion act together, although we study them separately for convenience.

Likewise, the two types of weathering, *physical weathering* (disintegration) and *chemical weathering* (decomposition), operate simultaneously, though one or the other—depending upon the nature of the rock and the particular climate—usually predominates.

PHYSICAL WEATHERING

Also called *mechanical weathering* and *disintegration,* physical weathering results in the breaking down of rock by various forces that proceed without changing the chemical composition of the material.

Temperature Changes. Rocks expand when heated and contract when cooled, though to a far less extent than most other substances. The component minerals vary in their coefficients of expansion, thereby setting up stresses within the rocks. A daily and seasonal repetition of this process over the centuries causes small cracks to develop which permit the entrance of moisture and the beginning of plant growth. These last are vastly more effective as agents of weathering than the actual changes in the volume of the rock, which are slight.

Frost Action or Wedging. Dew, rain, and snow seep into rock cracks and pores near the surface of the ground. When it freezes, the 9 per cent expansion of this water exerts an enclosed pressure of thousands of pounds per square inch. This is a powerful mechanism for shattering porous, jointed, and weakened rock. The same process, when the force is directed upward in loose rock, is known as *frost heaving*; it brings boulders to the surface of farmland after the winter and causes roads to bulge.

Exfoliation. Alternate expansion and contraction in the outer part of a rock body, together with freezing and thawing, causes the spalling (chipping) off of scales and slabs, a process known as *exfoliation*. In this way, when aided by minor chemical changes, angular masses take on curved outlines, referred to as *spheroidal weathering*. *Granular disintegration* sheds rock fragments over the ground, sometimes nearly burying large rounded boulders in their own debris.

EXAMPLES: The rounded surface of Half Dome in Yosemite National Park, consisting of sheet-like curved slabs of rock, has been described as due to exfoliation, as has Stone Mountain near Atlanta, Georgia, and famed Sugar Loaf in the harbor of Rio de Janeiro, Brazil. Geologists are, however, not agreed that exfoliation on such a large scale is due to weathering.

Plants and Animals. Pressures comparable to those of freezing water are exerted in crevices by the roots of trees. Even small plants are effective in weathering. Animals that tramp upon the ground or churn it up by burrowing aid in the mechanical destruction of rock.

CHEMICAL WEATHERING

Chemical weathering, also called *decomposition*, gives birth to new minerals in place of the ones it destroys. Chemically active gases in the atmosphere combine with elements in the minerals, yielding new and usually simpler compounds. The soluble constituents are removed by *leaching* (percolation of water, which absorbs solubles). Plants play a part in the chemical decay of rock substances.

Hydration. The addition of water by chemical means produces hydrous oxides and hydrous silicates from the common minerals of the crust. In this fashion, especially, feldspar is converted to kaolin and other clay minerals of tremendous significance because they are the basis of the soil which supports all life on the land. By means of this and similar chemical changes, the loosened rock material swells and expands physically at the same time.

Oxidation. The addition of oxygen alone (*oxidation*) is aided by the presence of moist air. Iron compounds, especially pyrite, are those most affected by oxidation. Color changes result and acids are released in a never ending chain of reactions.

Carbonation. Carbon dioxide is added to rock minerals (*carbonation*) in the form of carbonic acid, which has derived its CO_2 content from the atmosphere and vegetation. Carbonic acid is much more effective than pure water in attacking feldspar and other minerals. Silica and potassium-sodium carbonates are thus dissolved.

RATE OF WEATHERING

Although certain types of rock are long-lasting, even the most resistant rock will finally weather away. Furthermore, the different kinds of rocks weather unequally, in response to the following factors: (1) mineral or chemical composition, (2) temperature, (3) moisture, (4) altitude, and (5) plant and animal life. The softer and the more soluble parts of a rock body disappear most readily by *differential weathering*. The disposition of a fragmental rock such as sandstone depends largely upon the nature of the bonding material; a soluble cement will dissolve, but a firmly compacted rock may hold together for a long time.

Physical weathering is relatively more operative in cold and dry climates, where the warmth and humidity which promote chemical weathering are not present to a significant degree. In polar latitudes, on high mountains, and in deserts, freshly broken rock is strewn over the landscape, remaining there for prolonged periods before it decomposes. Frost action is largely responsible for the debris; the freezing point is reached nightly in typical mountain and desert areas. On the other hand, the effect of plant roots is minimized by the scarcity of vegetation. Shale, being the least resistant of rocks under both humid and arid conditions, distintegrates readily, hence often underlies valleys or lowlands. Quartzite, at the opposite extreme, stands up as ridges almost everywhere, regardless of the climatic conditions.

In regions with much rainfall, particularly in the tropics, chemical weathering proceeds rapidly and extends to several hundred feet. This weathering is more effective in rolling topography at moderate altitudes. Limestone and dolomite are particularly

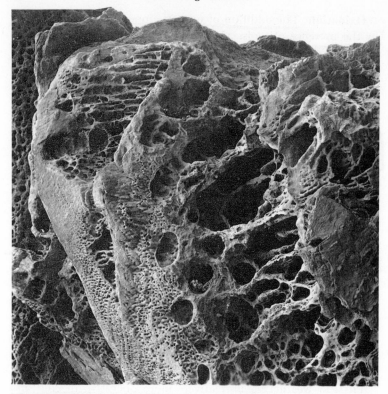

U. S. Geological Survey
Walcott
FIG. 17—Differential weathering in sandstone.

susceptible to being dissolved in a moist climate, leaving clay-covered lowlands, whereas in arid lands they are more resistant and generally endure as bare ridges and peaks. Granite tends to weather more readily in an arid climate where its coarse-grained texture and complex mineral make-up render it more prone to attack by the processes of physical disintegration.

SOILS

Soil consists of broken and decomposed rock, with added products of decaying organic matter, called *humus,* from previous generations of plants. The factors that determine the specific kind of soil that will develop are the following: (1) kind of original rock, (2) slope of the land, (3) climate, (4) plant and animal life, and (5) time of exposure. The relative importance of these factors is much disputed.

A soil begins at the surface and extends downward at the expense of the *bedrock* which furnishes it. A *mature soil,* in which continued downward growth balances erosion at the top, has a *soil profile* consisting of three layers, or *horizons,* as follows:

A-horizon, or *topsoil,* from which fine matter is carried down and soluble matter leached out; gray or black from humus.

B-horizon, or *subsoil,* in which the material brought down from above has accumulated.

C-horizon, of decayed parent rock, grading downward into unweathered bedrock.

The entire loose material, which lies upon the bedrock like a cloak, is appropriately known as the *mantle rock.*

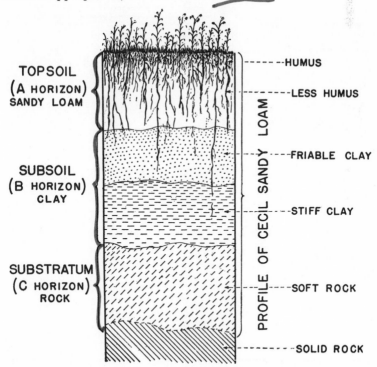

FIG. 18—Soil profile. (By permission from *Geology Principles and Processes,* 4th ed., by Emmons, Thiel, Stauffer, and Allison. Copyright, 1955. McGraw-Hill Book Co., Inc.)

Of the numerous types of soil classified by soil scientists, *laterite* is perhaps best known to geologists. This is a red or yellow soil, low in silica but high in iron and aluminum oxides and hydroxides. It has presumably been formed by intensive weathering in tropical climates having a heavy seasonal rainfall.

REVIEW QUESTIONS

1. What are the two principal kinds of weathering?
2. How is frost wedging accomplished?
3. Explain exfoliation.
4. What are the most important kinds of chemical weathering?
5. Sketch and label a soil profile showing the three main horizons.
6. Where is laterite found and what is its composition?

10
Gravity Movements

As they are broken up by weathering, the rocks of the earth's crust begin their movement toward the sea. Agents of erosion transport the rock debris, together with occasional large portions of detached bedrock, to lower places on the surface of the land and to the bottom of bodies of water. When gravity is the chief operating agent (i.e., when the action of streams, glaciers, wind, waves, or currents is not involved), the process of transportation is referred to as *mass movement, mass wasting,* or *downslope movement*. This movement is a factor in reducing the height of the continents, as well as furnishing further raw material for the other processes of erosion.

Gravity movements may occur in dry material or in that which is water-soaked. The rock may act as an elastic or rigid solid, a plastic substance, or a fluid. The velocity of rock movement ranges from imperceptibly slow to very rapid, as in an avalanche. Anything that reduces internal friction may initiate mass movement: heavy snow; rainwater when it lessens the cohesion of the soil and makes it heavier; oversteepening by other agents of erosion; or artificial construction.

The accumulation of rubble at the base of a cliff is known as *sliderock*. The term *talus* is applied to both the rock and the sloping surface produced by the process. Entire cliffs, in this way, are sometimes almost buried in their own debris. The slope of the lower part of the talus decreases and merges into the flatter country beyond.

SLOW MOVEMENTS

The quantitative importance of these nonspectacular slower movements of rock and soil is tremendous, though there is only indirect evidence of the transformation of the land by this means.

Creep. On any land surface except an absolutely flat one, the soil, even when protected by vegetation, moves downslope by slow plastic flowage, aided by moisture and other factors. In doing so, it bends down layers of rock and dislodges blocks from their outcrops, displaces fences and walls, and tilts gravestones. This migration is known as *creep*.

Solifluction. Water-saturated soil, subjected to alternate freezing and thawing, as in mountains and arctic regions, moves by the process of *solifluction*. Above the zone of "permanently" frozen ground (*permafrost*) the soil thaws seasonally from the surface downward. The melted ice cannot penetrate the still-frozen earth beneath, and hence the water-logged soil moves sluggishly down even the gentlest slope.

RAPID MOVEMENTS

The sudden movement of rock under the influence of gravity is one of the more catastrophic of Nature's activities. The most dramatic of surface earth movements is a *landslide,* or *avalanche.* A *rockslide* or *rockfall* is a slippage of bedrock along planes of weakness; the momentum developed may be sufficient to carry rock part way up the opposite wall of a valley. *Slump* is the downward and outward collapse of material along a surface that curves underneath a steep slope. A *mudflow* is the movement of loose material of varying consistency behaving more or less like a fluid mass as it advances down a small valley; it is most common in steep gulches in semi-arid regions when there is an exceptionally heavy rainfall. An *earthflow* is similar to a mudflow but involves less water and so is more sluggish.

EXAMPLES: Two disastrous landslides in the Rocky Mountains were those of Frank, Alberta, in 1903, and in the Gros Ventre Valley, Wyoming, in 1925. Mudflows and rock glaciers are common in the San Juan Mountains of southwest Colorado.

REVIEW QUESTIONS

1. Discuss gravity in relation to weathering.
2. What is talus?
3. Explain the origin of solifluction.
4. How do landslides, mudflows, and earthflows differ from one another?

11
Streams

The study of flowing water is the heart of physical geology. Fed by a multiplicity of sources but confined to definite channels, streams, aided by the gravity movements discussed in Chapter 10, have been the chief agents in the sculpturing of the landscape. Even in the most arid parts of the world the principal topographic features are a consequence of stream erosion. Stream action, moreover, gave us the first vital clues to earth history by revealing the continuity of geologic processes.

SOURCES OF STREAM WATER

Streams obtain practically all their water from precipitation in the form of rain and snow. Most of this water re-enters the atmosphere by *evaporation* from vegetation, the soil, and water bodies, or by the *transpiration* of plants which have taken it up. Some of the water proceeds to sink into the earth by *infiltration* and becomes the *ground water* discussed in Chapter 12; much of this eventually enters streams. Some of the precipitated water is temporarily locked up in snow fields and glaciers (see Chapter 13), to be released later by evaporation or melting. The rest of the water flows off the land as *runoff*, the proportion of which varies according to many factors, such as wind, humidity, vegetation, rock types, and relief. This runoff starts as a thin film called *sheet wash*, combined with a network of tiny rills, together constituting *sheet runoff;* when this water is concentrated in a channel, a stream has its birth.

KINDS OF STREAMS

A *stream* is a body of water flowing in a channel; it may be called a "river," a "creek," or a "brook." Streams vary greatly in size, velocity, spacing, clearness, and every other characteristic.

A *permanent, or perennial, stream* is one that flows throughout the year because its bed traverses a zone where the ground water table comes to the surface of the land (see page 119). A *temporary*, or *intermittent, stream* carries water only part of the time because it is dependent upon precipitation or melting snow or ice; an *ephemeral stream* depends entirely upon precipitation.

A stream that follows the initial or original slope of the land is called a *consequent stream.* The streams flowing seaward down a newly elevated area of sea bottom (coastal plain) with its seaward dipping gently inclined strata provide the best example of a consequent stream. Where layers of rock are tilted, the softer layers erode into valleys while the harder ones stand as ridges; tributaries to a main stream tend to follow the soft rock belts and are called *subsequent streams* since their courses are controlled by the rock structure and developed after the initial consequent drainage. An *obsequent stream* flows down the back of such a ridge, opposite in direction to the consequent stream and at right angles to the subsequent stream. When a stream maintains its course in spite of later earth movements or impeding lava flows, it is called an *antecedent stream.* A stream that originates under one set of conditions (such as composition or structure of rock) and cuts its channel into the buried older rocks of a quite different kind or structure, is known as a *superimposed* or *superposed stream.*

GROWTH OF STREAMS

As water accumulates in miniature channels, called *rills,* the embryonic stream begins to enlarge the depression it occupies. It works simultaneously in four directions. The channel is deepened and widened; it is lengthened toward the mouth of the stream, which is forced to extend the channel downslope, and it is also lengthened headward, as more water falls into the upper part of the leaf-shaped *drainage basin.*

The typical branching pattern of a stream, with the tributaries arranged like the limbs of a tree, is called *dendritic* (treelike). Such a stream develops where the underlying rock is fairly uniform and does not determine the direction of valley growth; granite and horizontal sedimentary rocks yield this type of stream pattern. When there are differences in the resistance of underlying folded rocks, an angular or rectilinear stream pattern is often produced, with a *trellis drainage,* in which the chief tributaries of the master stream follow parallel zones of least resistance. Streams that radiate outward from a high central zone, such as a volcanic cone, show a *radial* pattern.

Each stream grows at the expense of others. When a stream becomes dominant—because it contains more water, works in softer rocks, or descends a steeper slope—its faster headward erosion may enable it to undercut the divide separating it from another stream, thereby capturing the water belonging to the latter and diverting it to a new course. This process is known as *piracy,* and the victim is said to have been *beheaded.* Such is the common fate of many streams, and what were once *water gaps* at points where antecedent or superimposed streams flowed across narrow resistant ridges are now abandoned *wind gaps.*

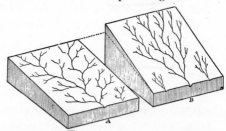

Fig. 19—Dendritic drainage development on homogeneous rocks (A) of gentle slope, (B) of steeper slope. (By permission from Worcester, Philip G., *Textbook of Geomorphology,* 2nd ed., copyright, 1948, D. Van Nostrand Company, Inc., Princeton, New Jersey.)

EXAMPLES: The Delaware Water Gap confines the Delaware River where it crosses the great quartzite ridge of Kittatinny Mountain. Historic Cumberland Gap in the Appalachian Mountains is a wind gap.

STREAM FLOW

Particles of water that move in parallel paths are said to show *laminar,* or *streamline, flow.* When the water begins to eddy and swirl and the individual particles do not move in a parallel direction, *turbulent flow* results. This turbulence increases with the velocity but mostly with the friction, and so is ordinarily greatest near the banks and bed of the stream. The swift movement of a stream over a waterfall produces *jet,* or *shooting, flow.*

The stream and its channel are reciprocally related, each intimately dependent upon and influencing the other. The hydraulic factors involved include the following:

1. *Channel size*. The cross-sectional area (channel size) of a stream is the product of the mean width times the mean depth.

2. *Channel shape*. This refers to the *cross* (or *transverse*) *profile* as measured from side to side along the bottom. A rectangular channel has a greater contact surface, or *wetted perimeter* (width plus twice the depth), than a curved channel. The greater contact surface of the rectangular channel adds to the friction and turbulence.

3. *Channel slope*. Also known as *gradient* and measured in feet per mile, this refers to the descent along the *long*, or *longitudinal profile*, as measured downstream at intervals from source to mouth.

4. *Velocity*. The speed of flow may be measured with a current meter inserted for readings at numerous stations.

5. *Discharge*. This is the quantity of water (in cubic feet per second) passing a given spot in a unit of time. It equals average velocity times cross-sectional area and fluctuates continuously, especially seasonally.

6. *Load*. This consists of the total material carried (1) in solution, (2) as sediment, and (3) as larger movable fragments.

STREAM ENERGY

Streams can best be studied by considering their energy and its effects. The energy of a stream is its ability to perform work, and a stream's work consists of the removal of rock, sediment, and dissolved matter. When a stream has a large amount of energy, it is an effective agent of erosion; when a stream has a small amount of energy, it is an agent of deposition; a stream in equilibrium, being just able to carry its load, is said to be *graded*, or *at grade*. In a system so complex as a stream and its tributaries, which in their response to the environment act almost like one gigantic organism, precise or even approximate equilibrium is an extremely sensitive condition, subject to rapid changes with almost every wind that blows and every drop of water that falls. The numerous factors involved in the hydrologic cycle (from precipitation to evaporation) are still little understood by geologists and hydraulic engineers.

STREAM EROSION

Rock material is removed from the surrounding terrain by a combination of several stream processes which act concurrently.

Sheet Erosion. Sheet runoff contributes a substantial amount of sediment to streams, picking up and transporting particles in its path as it moves down the slopes.

Hydraulic Plucking. The pressure of the water itself against cracks in the rock compresses the air within them and serves to quarry out blocks of various dimensions. Soft stream banks are often undercut by flowing water alone. A whirling eddy of water lifts loose particles, especially those that are somewhat rounded and uniformly sized and are not too firmly packed, and turbulence may scour the channel clean.

Abrasion, or Corrasion. The erosive power of a stream is determined largely by its content of sediment; clear water is a relatively ineffective agent of erosion. The "tools" of a stream are the fragments that it carries, and these in turn are abraded and reduced in size by the force of contact. When a single boulder or collection of gravel is swirled in a hollow in the bedrock long enough, a kettle-shaped depression called a *pothole* may be formed; the exposed beds of some dry streams seem to be a succession of such holes.

Solution, or Corrosion. The dissolving action of a stream depends upon the kind of rock it traverses; limestone and dolomite, especially, are fairly soluble in acid waters. Most of the dissolved matter in a stream, however, is supplied by underground water draining into it.

STREAM TRANSPORTATION

The burden of material carried by a stream from its point of erosion to its place of deposition is called the *stream load*. In addition to sheet runoff and the actual erosion of the stream in its channel, there are other sources of sediment found in streams. (1) Gravity pulls down loose material dislodged by the various types of weathering (see Chapter 9)—this process is of overwhelming importance. (2) Wind blows sand and silt into the stream. (3) Volcanic dust and ash are present everywhere, though much more abundant in certain regions. (4) Melting glaciers quickly overload a stream with their powdered rock. (5) Floating ice, driftwood, and other obstructions chip away at the banks and add material for the water to take away.

Streams transport their load by traction, solution, and suspension.

Traction. Large angular fragments often slide along the bed of the stream, and rounded fragments are rolled along the bottom. The motion is seldom uniform and depends on the velocity of the stream and the nature of the flow. All this material that moves in the lower part of the stream constitutes its *bed load.*

Suspension. Uplifted into the main current of a stream, out of contact with the bed, is the *suspended load,* consisting of sediment that will settle out upon standing. Turbulence being greater in the lower levels, the coarser particles move in that zone. The total amount of sediment in suspension increases downstream as more tributaries enter.

Solution. Dissolved matter, though invisible, may represent a large proportion of the total load of a stream, particularly if it is fed by subsurface water coming from a region of carbonate and other soluble rocks.

Effects of Flood. The *capacity* of a stream, which is the amount of material that it can transport under given circumstances, and the *competence,* which is the maximum size of a particle that it can move, are both increased enormously in time of flood. The size (diameter) of particles a stream can carry increases as the square of the velocity. If the velocity of the current is tripled, fragments nine times the size (the square of three) can be carried, and the abrasive power is likewise multiplied by nine. These figures vary according to a number of factors, but since flood waters may travel at many times the speed of an ordinary river, the enormously damaging effect of a flood can be understood.

STREAM DEPOSITION

If the conditions which enable a stream to transport its load are reversed, the stream will proceed to deposit instead. All stream deposits are termed *alluvium.* Stream deposition occurs as a result of (1) a decline in gradient, (2) a reduction in velocity, or (3) a decrease in volume. These changes are produced by numerous factors, such as evaporation, freezing, variation in valley shape, encounters with obstacles, and entrance into standing water. Owing to the density of water, deposition from it is highly selective, the coarsest and heaviest material settling out first.

Stream deposition is conveniently divided into (1) deposits made within the stream valley itself, (2) alluvial fans, and (3) deposits in bodies of water.

Deposits in Valleys. The alluvium laid down in the channel of a stream is called *channel fill;* accumulations of this fill take many shapes, but are generally known as *river bars* or *sand bars*. These collect along the edges of the stream (particularly at the inner side of every sharp bend), around obstructions, and as submerged shoals and low islands in the stream. When a stream is excessively overloaded, alluvium is rapidly deposited in constantly shifting positions and the stream is obliged to split into interlacing channels which separate and unite (*anastomose*) in such a way that the name *braided stream* is appropriate. A stream that alternately erodes and deposits under rapidly changing conditions produces an effect known as *scour and fill.*

EXAMPLE: The South Platte River in Nebraska is an ideal braided stream.

After a flood has receded from its high-water stage, alluvium is left upon the level ground or *floodplain* on both sides of a stream. This creates a *floodplain deposit,* which increases in thickness with each subsequent higher flood. Floodplain deposits are thickest at the margins of the channel, and slope gradually away from the stream. *Natural levees* are the low embankments originating in this way along the margins of a river; they serve to protect the flat land beyond, though if perforated in time of flood they allow the water to surge into the low part of the floodplain away from the river.

EXAMPLE: The natural levees of the Mississippi River are so high that the Yazoo River is unable to enter and has to run parallel to it for about 200 miles.

A stream may later excavate part of its floodplain, leaving terraces standing above its new level. Terraces develop first in the lower reaches of a stream and then extend upstream, passing into the normal floodplain in either direction. They may be *unpaired terraces,* or they may be *paired terraces,* matching in height on both sides of the stream. Some alluvial terraces are protected from destruction by hard rock beneath, becoming *rock-defended,* or *rock-perched, terraces.*

Alluvial Fans. Where a stream leaves the mountains and emerges onto the plains or a wide valley, it undergoes a sudden decrease in velocity. This causes the deposition of alluvium in a fan-shaped body, called an *alluvial fan.* As the fan grows steeper, thicker, and coarser, it takes on a conical shape and is termed an *alluvial cone.*

The merger of adjacent alluvial fans from parallel streams forms a connected undulating sheet of sediment along the base of a mountain range. Several names are given to this topographic feature: *piedmont alluvial plain, compound alluvial fan, alluvial apron,* or simply the Spanish word *bajada.*

EXAMPLE: Extensive bajadas are found along the isolated mountain ranges of the Basin and Range province in Nevada and adjoining states.

U. S. Geological Survey   *Balsley*

Fig. 20—Alluvial fans. Mojave Desert, California.

Deposits in Water. Deposited in water, the counterpart of an alluvial fan is a *delta;* so named from the resemblance of certain deltas, specifically that of the Nile, to the shape of the Greek letter (Δ), with the apex pointing upstream. Deltas result from the abrupt decline in the energy of a stream where it flows into a body of standing water such as a lake or ocean. Some deltas have even formed in rivers where a swift tributary enters the slower main stream.

EXAMPLES: The Nile has the best known of the world's deltas; those of the Mississippi, Danube, and Ganges-Brahmaputra are also outstanding.

As the delta grows seaward, the stream itself breaks up into minor channels called *distributaries,* which radiate from the original stream, shifting position from time to time, and winding between natural levees.

As seen in cross section, a well-formed delta reveals three sets of sediment arranged in a definite pattern. The bulk of the delta consists of coarser material inclined forward at the angle of repose (about 35 degrees); these beds are the *foreset beds.* Fine silt is carried farther out, where it settles on the bottom of the lake or sea as flat-lying *bottomset beds.* An upper veneer of sediment makes the *topset beds,* upon which the stream water flows.

CYCLES OF EROSION

The features that develop on any particular landscape depend upon a combination of (1) the structure of the rocks, (2) the geologic processes acting upon them, and (3) the extent to which the geologic agents have performed their work.

A new stream, or a land area newly exposed to erosion, passes through a continuous sequence of change that constitutes its cycle of erosion, or *geomorphic cycle.* The successive stages in this cycle, referred to under three main categories as *youth, maturity,* and *old age,* are identified by certain distinctive characteristics, not by the passage of any definite interval of time.

The principal features of the geomorphic cycle are generally recognizable, though many geologists protest the abuse of this concept when it is oversimplified and applied to every place on the globe. If we are aware of its limitations, deal with it descriptively rather than quantitatively, realize the differences due to climate, and distinguish between the age of a stream and the age

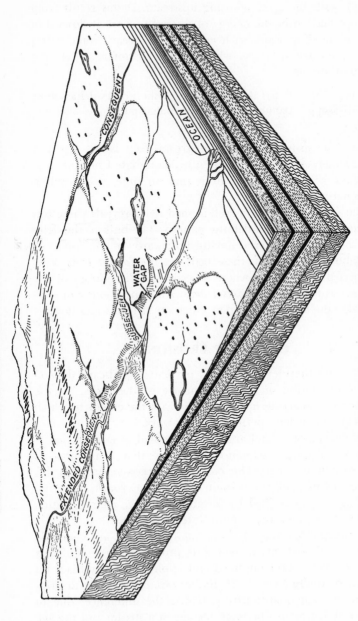

FIG. 21—Stream development in coastal-plain topography. Consequent and subsequent streams. (Drawings by Elizabeth Burckmyer. By permission from von Engeln, O. D., *Geomorphology*, copyright, 1942, The Macmillan Co., New York.)

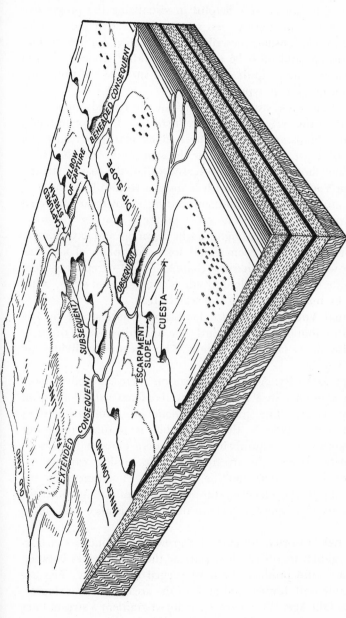

Fig. 22—Advanced stage: Erosion has brought land into relief; a broad low-land has been opened up. Subsequent stream has beheaded a parallel consequent. Obsequent streams are developing valleys on and across the escarpment slopes of the cuestas. (By permission from von Engeln, O. D., *Geomorphology*, copyright, 1942, The Macmillan Co., New York.)

of the region through which it flows, the concept of the geo-morphic cycle can be very helpful in visualizing the progressive changes that occur more or less systematically with the lapse of time. The cycle is usually described, as it is below, for a temperate humid region, and must be modified for other climates. It also is based upon rapid uplift of a new land surface, but this situation is not necessarily typical.

The stream cycle usually, though not always, advances more rapidly than the *cycle of regional reduction,* so that, for instance, a youthful landscape may be traversed by mature streams. All sections of a stream do not age at the same rate, and the tributaries often show more youthful features than the master stream.

Stream Youth. Beginning with *infancy,* a youthful stream is an actively eroding one. Its dominant cutting is downward between steepening canyon cliffs. The cross profile is usually V-shaped, but the walls may be straight, as in a gorge, and occasionally even overhanging. No room is left for a floodplain of any size, and the water fills the narrow channel nearly or entirely from side to side. The longitudinal profile is irregular and steep, being marked by numerous rapids and waterfalls.

Regional Youth. A youthful landscape is intersected by few and small tributaries; consequently the upland is poorly drained, containing many lakes and swamps. The interstream divides are high and wide.

Stream Maturity. As sideward erosion increases and a flood-plain accumulates in a broad and well-defined valley, a stream becomes mature. The gradient is moderate, eliminating most rapids and waterfalls. As the graded state is attained, the lower courses approach an equilibrium between erosion and deposition; irregularities deflect the stream from side to side, causing the formation of *meanders* and the deposition of sediment on the floodplain. During this stage the stream etches out its most pic-turesque scenery from the rocks of unequal resistance and unlike structure.

Regional Maturity. An extensive growth of tributaries charac-terizes regional maturity; these narrow the high divides between the streams and produce the most rugged topography. The up-land is now well drained and most of the area consists of slopes.

Stream Old Age. With a greatly reduced gradient a stream loses its ability to erode, except laterally, and deposits instead. The aged stream meanders sluggishly over its broad floodplain as it moves within its *meander belt* in a wide and shallow valley. Meanders are accentuated as time passes, producing hairpin curves which migrate slowly downstream; finally the stream may break across the narrow neck of land at the base of the loop, making a *cutoff* if by encroachment and a *chute* if by flood. The *abandoned meander* remains for a while as an *oxbow lake* but eventually silts up to become a *bayou* or swamp.

EXAMPLE: Mark Twain, in *Life on the Mississippi*, devoted an interesting chapter to the development of cutoffs in that most notable example of a meandering stream.

Regional Old Age. An old landscape has a few large streams flowing between low, narrow divides. There are no mountains or high hills. The ultimate result, if carried to completion, is the nearly level surface of large extent known as a *peneplane*, above which rise low, isolated erosion remnants called *monadnocks*.

EXAMPLE: The origin of several of the major peneplanes in North America is described in Chapter 24. Mount Monadnock in New Hampshire, one of the familiar peaks in the eastern states, gave its name to this feature.

Rivers that run into the sea can deepen their valleys only until they reach sea level, which is considered the *base level* of erosion. (There are certain complications: a stream must have some gradient in order to flow at all; some rivers are strong enough to push aside the ocean water; and sea level itself is not stationary.) A stream that enters another body of water, such as a lake or another stream, does so at the level of that body as its *temporary*, or *local, base level*. This level is effective until the lake or the main stream is lowered.

Arid Cycle. The enclosed drainage of many desert basins goes through a cycle different from that described for humid climates. It is more dependent upon local base levels, some of which may be below sea level. Runoff is inadequate to remove all the sediment supplied by the processes of slope erosion, and so it accumulates to considerable thicknesses, perhaps nearly burying the mountain remnants which remain. Often a smooth rock-cut surface, called a *pediment*, extends outward from the bare cliffs above, passing beneath the rock debris which buries it lower down; this is often considered to be the arid-land equivalent of a peneplane.

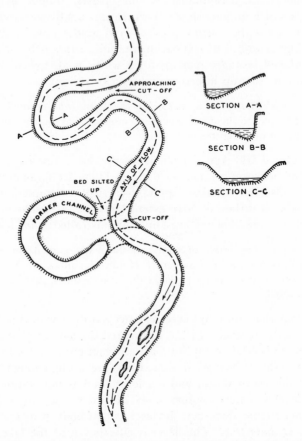

Fig. 23—Meandering stream, plan view and profiles. (*After Thomas and White.*) (By permission from *Geology Principles and Processes,* 4th ed., by Emmons, Thiel, Stauffer, and Allison. Copyright, 1955. McGraw-Hill Book Co., Inc.)

Interrupted Cycles. The normal cycle of erosion may be interrupted at any stage. Interference by (1) diastrophism, (2) glaciation, (3) wind, (4) vulcanism, (5) subsurface drainage, (6) ocean waves and currents, and (7) climatic changes can cause the cycle to be hastened or part of it to be repeated.

Diastrophism (see p. 18), bringing changes in the relation of land to sea, is the dominant process involved in an interrupted cycle of erosion. When the land sinks, the stream ages more quickly because it now has less rock surface to destroy before peneplanation. A rise in sea level has the same effect. Either change results in the flooding of the lower ends of stream valleys along the coastline. This produces *drowned valleys* and leaves their now isolated tributaries as *dismembered streams.*

EXAMPLE: Chesapeake Bay is the drowned valley of the Susquehanna River and its former tributaries, including the Potomac.

The opposite movement, an *uplift* of the land relative to sea level, increases the gradient and gives the stream renewed energy. This process is termed *rejuvenation,* the start of a new cycle of erosion. A V-shaped notch, typical of a youthful stream, will be incised into the older stream valley, probably leaving terraces on both sides. Unless tilting is involved, the rejuvenation migrates slowly upstream as a *nickpoint.* If the rejuvenated stream was a meandering one, the curving pattern will be preserved within steep walls, producing *incised,* or *intrenched, meanders;* later undercutting of the neck of such a meander is one way in which *natural bridges* are formed.

EXAMPLES: The "goosenecks" of the San Juan River in southeastern Utah show incised meanders on a grand scale; the superb natural bridges of several national monuments in Utah have a related origin.

REVIEW QUESTIONS

1. How does a stream obtain its energy?
2. What happens to the water that falls as rain?
3. How does laminar flow differ from turbulent flow?
4. What effect does the shape of the channel have upon stream flow?
5. What is the geologic difference between a permanent stream and a temporary stream?
6. What is a subsequent stream and why is it often found in a valley between two ridges?
7. Draw the dendritic, trellis, and radial stream patterns and tell where each one occurs.
8. By what means does a stream erode its channel?
9. What causes a braided stream?

10. How do natural levees originate?
11. Draw the cross section of a delta and name its parts.
12. Outline the cycle of stream erosion.
13. How can rejuvenation take place?

12
Ground Water

The portion of the hydrosphere that occupies open spaces within the lithosphere makes up the great domain of ground water, also known as *underground, subsurface,* and *subterranean water.* Of incalculable value for everyday rural and urban life, modern industry, and irrigation, ground water is usually taken for granted, even by those whose activities most depend upon it.

There are three sources of ground water, as follows:

1. Precipitation, or *meteoric water,* is the major source of ground water. Rain and snow that does not evaporate or run off in streams infiltrates the pores and cracks in the soil and bedrock. Some of it may later, of course, reach the atmosphere or join bodies of flowing or standing water.

2. Water trapped in sedimentary deposits while they are being formed is termed *connate water.* This is often salty because the majority of sedimentary rocks were deposited beneath sea water.

3. Magmatic and volcanic activity adds water to both the shallow rocks and the surface. This is referred to as *magmatic water* or, because it is presumably just beginning to circulate freely, *juvenile water.* It mixes with ground water from other sources and soon loses its identity; the heat associated with it may cause other water to boil out of the rocks in the form of hot springs or geysers.

GROUND WATER ZONES

The water-bearing ground beneath the exposed surface of the earth consists of two major zones, the vadose zone and the zone of saturation.

Vadose Zone. Descending water passes through an upper layer of soil and rock in which the spaces are filled partly with air and partly with water. This is the *vadose zone,* or *zone of aeration.* The *belt of soil moisture* supplies water to growing plants, and the lower margin, the *capillary fringe,* keeps water from sinking

119

downward. Between these layers there is an intermediate belt in which drops of water are virtually suspended by the molecular attraction between them and the adjacent rock surface, except when flushed downward in times of rain or melting snow.

Zone of Saturation. Beneath the vadose zone is the *zone of*

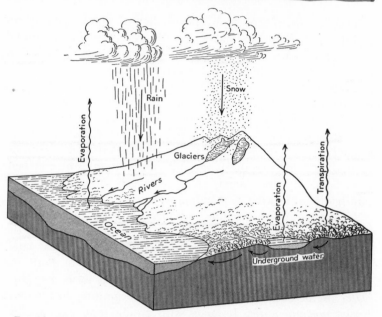

Fig. 24—The hydrologic cycle. (L. Don Leet and Sheldon Judson, *Physical Geology,* 2nd ed., 1958 by Prentice-Hall, Inc., Englewood Cliffs, New Jersey. Reproduced by permission of the publisher.)

saturation, extending to a considerable depth, in which cracks and holes in the rock are completely filled with water. The boundary between these two main zones is an uneven surface called the *water table.* The water table must be penetrated to provide a dependable well or a permanent stream. It is spoken of as a subdued replica of the topography because it tends to follow the contours of the ground surface, rising under hills and descending under valleys. The water table is close to the surface in moist climates, and far below it in arid regions. If the water table is not replenished, usage lowers it. As a well is pumped, a *cone of depression* forms immediately surrounding it, lowering the water table toward the center.

MOVEMENT OF GROUND WATER

Water descends through the vadose zone to the water table, the slope of which is termed the *hydraulic gradient*. Through the zone of saturation most of the water moves downward toward the stream valleys that intersect the water table. The streams are fed by this subterranean water supply, except in arid regions, where the reverse may be true. If precipitation were to cease, the water table would eventually flatten out.

Ground water does not travel uniformly through all types of rock. Two concepts, porosity and permeability, should be understood as factors in this variation.

Porosity. The percentage of a rock or soil that is represented by open spaces is its *porosity*. The porosity of sediments and sedimentary rocks depends upon the shape, relative sizes, and arrangement of the grains, and the degree of compaction and cementation. Rocks of any kind contain more water when they have been cracked or partially dissolved. The range of porosity in rocks is wide, from a fraction of one per cent for fresh igneous rocks to 90 per cent for newly settled mud.

Permeability. The ability of a rock to transmit water under pressure is its *permeability*. A rock must be porous to be permeable, but the reverse is not necessarily true. For instance, the abundant gas cavities of pumice are not connected; specimens may therefore float for years before becoming waterlogged. A moist and porous clay is relatively *impermeable* because the minute flakes hold the drops of water firmly by molecular attraction; a coarser and less porous gravel is much more permeable. Unconsolidated sand, imperfectly cemented sandstone, and certain kinds of limestone, the open spaces of which are due largely to solution, are other permeable rocks.

When a permeable area of limited extent traps water in the vadose zone, above the general level of the water table, this isolated body of saturated ground has a *perched water table* and may be an important though local source of water.

Aquifers. A permeable material through which ground water travels into wells and springs is called an *aquifer*. Inclined beds of rock provide a difference in pressure, known as *head,* between the place of intake and the place of discharge. Some formations carry water at a rate almost infinitesimally slow; others, at a velocity exceeding several hundred feet per day.

When a dipping aquifer, which receives water at its upper ends, is sandwiched between two impermeable layers, the confined ground water may be under considerable pressure as it percolates through the rock. If it reaches a natural or artificial opening that will allow it to escape upward, either a flowing *spring* or an *artesian well* is formed. (An artesian well does not have to be deep, nor does the flow have to rise all the way to the surface.)

EXAMPLE: An artesian basin of great economic importance is fed by the Dakota sandstone, which underlies the North Central States and reaches the surface in the Black Hills and Rocky Mountains.

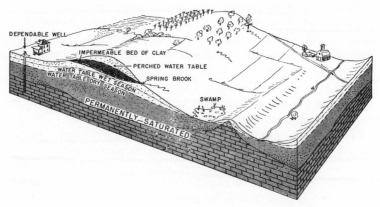

FIG. 25—Water table in relation to topography and structure. (By permission from *Geology*, by von Engeln and Caster. Copyright, 1952. McGraw-Hill Book Co., Inc.)

DISCHARGE OF GROUND WATER

Large quantities of water reach the surface of the earth by man-made wells, which are dug or drilled to various depths. However, ground water most commonly emerges from below the surface as *seepage*. It may join a stream, enter a lake or the ocean directly, or form a spring.

Springs. Springs usually make their appearance upon hillsides or in valleys but may issue almost anywhere, even beneath the sea. Springs range in volume from an occasional trickle that merely moistens the soil to a torrent that constitutes the source of a large river. They may be named according to their dominant minerals, such as sulfur springs, bitter springs, or lithia springs. A *mineral spring* is any spring with a considerable mineral content (all ground water contains some dissolved matter). Many hot springs are in volcanic regions; others are not and seem to owe their warmth to ordinary rain water which has descended to great depths before rising again.

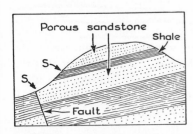
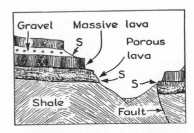
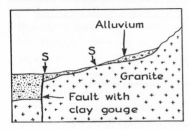
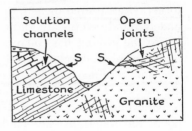

Fig. 26—Typical occurrences of springs. (By permission from *Principles of Geology*, 2nd ed., by J. Gilluly, A. C. Waters, and A. O. Woodford. San Francisco and London: W. H. Freeman and Company, 1959.)

EXAMPLE: The mineral water in Hot Springs National Park, Arkansas, is presumably ordinary rain water heated by a deep-seated igneous body during its passage through the rocks.

Geysers. A hot spring that erupts intermittently is a *geyser*. The volume and interval vary greatly; a few geysers are remarkably uniform in their activity. A geyser must be adjacent to a substantial source of heat, such as a cooling magma in an area of dying vulcanism. It also must have a complex system of subterranean conduits, which hinder circulation and permit the accumulation of water until it is heated above its normal boiling point. When this reservoir is disturbed, perhaps by spouting of superheated water near the surface, the pressure is reduced and the entire column below flashes into steam and bursts into eruption.

EXAMPLES: The three great geyser regions of the world are Yellowstone National Park, New Zealand (North Island), and Iceland.

EROSION DUE TO GROUND WATER

Ground water is an effective agent of erosion because it is charged with carbonic acid (contained in rain water), which dissolves carbonate rocks such as limestone, dolomite, and marble. Rock salt and gypsum are likewise soluble in ground water, the former even in pure water, but limestone is so abundant that the effective work of subsurface water is largely concentrated in it.

As water from rain and snow descends into the earth through cracks in the rock, the physical and chemical action of the water enlarges the cracks. Thus it tends to isolate blocks of rock and form cavities around them, into which surface water drains. Large underground caverns are formed by this process, and eventually, where the ground has collapsed into the hollows beneath, surface depressions develop, called *sinks*, *sinkholes*, or *swallow holes*. The outlets of many of these are choked with debris, so that lakes are formed. In time, an area of tunnels, grottoes, and natural bridges comes into existence, replete with underground streams, pools, and waterfalls. The landscape developed in this way in a limestone area is known as *karst topography*, named from the Karst region of Yugoslavia and Italy.

TRANSPORTATION BY GROUND WATER

Limestone is carried in solution, in ground water, in the form of calcium bicarbonate, a compound resulting from the interaction of water, carbon dioxide from the atmosphere and vegetation, and the calcite grains of which limestone is composed. Although ground water normally erodes by its dissolving action, some actual abrasion is accomplished when it moves as an underground stream.

DEPOSITION BY GROUND WATER

The mineral content of ground water (calcium bicarbonate, iron and siliceous substances, and other compounds) may be deposited at any point along its route of travel. Acidic waters become neutralized by reaction with carbonate rock; mineral matter in solution is then precipitated between the grains of sediments, serving to cement them together. This process, taking place in the *zone of cementation,* is of the utmost importance in converting loose sediment into firm rock. In arid climates ground water is drawn upward to the surface, where it evaporates, leaving a coating of *alkali* (any bitter-tasting salt) or *caliche* (calcium carbonate).

Chemical precipitation often takes place around a nucleus, such as a grain of sand or a fossil, producing a nodule called a *concretion,* which may be of almost any size and shape. Concretions may grow at the expense of the surrounding rock, slowly

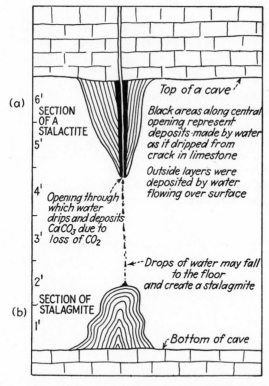

Top of a cave

(a)   SECTION OF A STALACTITE

Black areas along central opening represent deposits made by water as it dripped from crack in limestone

Outside layers were deposited by water flowing over surface

Opening through which water drips and deposits $CaCO_3$ due to loss of CO_2

Drops of water may fall to the floor and create a stalagmite

(b)   SECTION OF STALAGMITE

Bottom of cave

Fig. 27—Origin of stalactite and stalagmite. (By permission from *Introduction to Geology,* by Branson, Tarr, and Keller. Copyright, 1952. McGraw-Hill Book Co., Inc.)

replacing it by simultaneous solution and deposition; however, replacement is more characteristic of petrified wood, in which silica has been substituted for organic matter. Rounded cavities in rocks may be lined with projecting crystals or filled with minerals; these hollow crystal-lined cavities are known as *geodes*.

The most conspicuous effects of ground water deposition are found in caverns in the vadose zone, above the water table. Here percolating water evaporates, precipitating calcium carbonate as grotesque or beautiful *dripstone* decorations in the interior of the cave. *Stalactites* hang like icicles from the roof, *stalagmites* build up from the floor, and the two may join to form *columns* or *pillars*.

EXAMPLE: The Carlsbad Caverns in New Mexico contain the most massive examples known of these cave features.

REVIEW QUESTIONS

1. What is the chief source of subsurface water?
2. How does connate water get into the rocks?
3. What is the origin of juvenile water?
4. What is the significance of the water table?
5. How does water move through the rocks?
6. Distinguish between porosity and permeability.
7. Sketch an aquifer and mark the possible site of an artesian well.
8. What makes a geyser erupt?
9. How does karst topography develop?
10. What causes stalactites?

13

Glaciation

We still live in the Great Ice Age. Although glaciation is slightly less than one-third as extensive as it once was, bodies of ice cover 10 per cent of the land surface of the globe. Glaciers are both a major result and a significant cause of our climate, which is ever changing in numerous short and long cycles superimposed upon one another in a most complex fashion. The scenery of one-fifth of the globe owes its origin and much of its magnificence to the icy masses which have eroded, transported, and deposited on a grand scale, overriding the landscape and designing it anew. Glaciers have removed the soil in some regions and have enriched it in others. Many commercial deposits of sand and gravel are due to the moving ice and its meltwater, and valuable water supplies are obtained from glacial formations. The fluctuating level of the sea, glaciers and icebergs, thick deposits of loess (see p. 157), the changed courses of rivers, and the Great Lakes (see p. 228) and countless other lakes and swamps (see Chapter 14) are among the effects of Pleistocene glaciation that are with us to the present day. (The geologic history of the Pleistocene epoch is summarized in Chapter 24.)

CAUSES OF GLACIATION

The ultimate cause or causes of glaciation are not known. There are two immediate causes: (1) an increase in precipitation, and (2) a decrease in summer temperature, so that melting of winter snow is decreased.

Many hypotheses of glacial origin have been proposed. Those most widely discussed include the following, to each of which simplified objections are presented:

1. Mountain-building and the rise of continents produces lower average temperatures throughout the world as the general altitude increases. (Objection: Short-interval repetition of recent glaciation is difficult to explain in this way.)

2. Increased solar radiation raises temperatures and so increases

cloudiness, which adds to the precipitation and at the same time retards the melting of snow in mountains and polar regions. (Objection: Long-interval spacing of past glaciations is difficult to explain on this basis.) Decreased solar radiation seems certain to reduce temperatures on the earth.

3. A combination of elevation and varying solar radiation brings on times of glaciation. (Objection: Large fluctuations in the sun's activity are unproved.)

4. The changing position of the earth relative to the sun decreases the heat received by parts of the planet. (Objection: Absence of regular intervals of glaciation during most of geologic time and simultaneous glaciation in both northern and southern hemisphere are difficult to explain.)

5. The movement of continents across the face of the earth. (Objection: Continental drift is still a highly controversial subject; see p. 17, 47.)

6. The decreased content of carbon dioxide and water vapor in the atmosphere increases heat radiation from the earth and brings on refrigeration. (Objection: Systematic variations in the composition of the air are unproved.)

BEGINNING OF GLACIERS

A prolonged excess of snowfall over melting results in the gradual accumulation of snow in a *snow field*. The lower edge of a permanent snow field is called the *snow line*. The weight of the snow compresses the lower layers, and there is a downward seeping and refreezing of surface water. Under pressure (which raises temperature), the snow melts and recrystallizes into small pellets of ice known ɔs *névé* or *firn*. Further consolidation changes the firn (which is, on the average, 100 feet deep) into solid ice. As the ice begins to move slowly under the influence of gravity, a glacier has its start. Where it breaks away from the less mobile snow or firn, one or more deep, gaping cracks, or *crevasses,* called the *bergschrund* (mountain crevasse) are formed.

The visible layering of a snow field or a glacier is due to alternate melting and freezing and to additions of dust, volcanic ash, and other substances from above. Bands are also present that represent shearing and differential movement within the glacier, as well as concentrations of debris in those zones.

GLACIAL MOVEMENT

The movement of glaciers is still not fully understood. Glacier movement is basically due to the plasticity of the deeper levels of ice in the *zone of flow;* the lower ice carries along the upper, brittle ice in the *zone of fracture.*

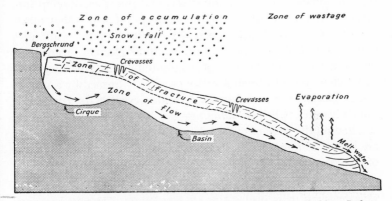

Fig. 28—Structure of a valley glacier. (L. Don Leet and Sheldon Judson, *Physical Geology,* 1954 by Prentice-Hall, Inc., Englewood Cliffs, New Jersey. Reproduced by permission of the publisher.)

Glacial movement is furthered by melting and refreezing and by expansion and contraction caused by slight changes in temperature. Ice crystals, and also blocks of ice, slip over each other under the influence of melting and pressure.

The rate of glacial movement varies from almost zero to (in rare instances) 100 or more feet per day. It is faster in the summer and during daylight. The rate is determined by measuring the change in position of large boulders on top of the glacier or of stakes that have been driven into the ice. Like a river, a glacier is slowed by friction; therefore, it moves more rapidly in the center than at the margins and on the surface than along the bottom.

When the glaciers are said to "advance" or "recede," what is referred to is the foot of the glacier, and not the entire glacier. A glacier which moves forward more rapidly than its terminus is melting is said to advance. A glacier recedes when its foot is melting back faster than the ice is moving forward. If the melting at the end of the glacier exactly balances the forward movement of the ice, the glacier appears to be stationary.

KINDS OF GLACIERS

Glaciers are classified as *valley glaciers, piedmont glaciers,* and *continental glaciers.* There seems little doubt that the various types originate in much the same way and that they develop into diverse forms according to the topography over which they move.

Valley Glaciers. Glaciers that are confined by the walls of a valley are called *valley, mountain,* or *alpine glaciers.* Originating in a snow field on the side of a mountain, this type of glacier moves downward through a valley previously formed by a stream. Valley glaciers are found in all latitudes, even at the equator at high altitudes. *Cliff,* or *hanging, glaciers* are glaciers that are perched on the edge of cliffs. Glaciers that terminate in the ocean are known as *tidal,* or *tidewater, glaciers* and are a prolific source of icebergs.

EXAMPLES: The high peaks of every continent except Australia contain valley glaciers; those in the Alps are best known. The west branch of the Hubbard Glacier in Alaska is 75 miles long. The Taku Glacier in Alaska is a typical tidal glacier.

Piedmont Glaciers. As a valley glacier reaches the flat land at the foot of the mountains where it is no longer confined by valley walls, it spreads out to form a broad apron of ice spoken of as a *piedmont glacier.*

EXAMPLE: The nearly stagnant Malaspina Glacier, the largest in Alaska, is fed by many valley glaciers emerging from the nearby mountains.

Continental Glaciers. The largest glaciers are the *continental glaciers, ice sheets,* or *icecaps.* A continental glacier moves in all directions away from its point of origin and completely covers the land except for isolated mountain peaks known as *nunataks,* which project above its surface. The term *icecap* is also used to describe a small glacier that spreads out from a center.

EXAMPLES: Antarctica and Greenland are now covered by continental glaciers, and Iceland has a number of icecaps, such as the Vatna Glacier, which remain from a former more extensive glaciation of the entire island.

GLACIAL EROSION

Glaciers are effective agents of erosion, especially in the mountains, where they have the advantage of exposed rock upon which to work. They erode by three processes: (1) *plucking,* or *quarrying* (the dislodging and transport of blocks of stone); (2) *abrasion,* the scratching and grinding of bedrock by rock fragments embedded in the bottom and sides of the glacier; and (3) simple *sweeping,* which cleans off any remaining debris.

Valley-Head Erosion. As meltwater sinks into cracks in the mountain side and freezes, it disrupts the bedrock underneath, preparing it for removal by the valley glacier. Many repetitions of this frost-wedging process carve out a hollow, shaped like the bowl of a steep-sided spoon, called a *cirque.* It rises abruptly above the valley and may be considered the starting place of the glacier. When the basin at the bottom of a cirque becomes filled with water, a mountain lake known as a *tarn* comes into existence. Cirques cut headward, so that those on opposite sides of a mountainous mass may nearly meet back to back; the knife-edged ridge between them is an *arête* (spine), or *serrate divide.* Where cirques actually meet and intersect, a mountain pass, or *col* (neck), is produced. Several glaciers eroding headward on various sides of a single peak may leave only a pointed spire, called a *horn,* standing in their midst.

EXAMPLES: The Continental Divide follows an imposing arête in Glacier National Park, Montana, known as the Garden Wall. The Matterhorn in the Swiss Alps is a perfect example of a glacial horn.

Valley-Wall Erosion. The stream valley which the glacier occupies is deepened and conspicuously widened, so that the previous youthful V-shaped valley becomes U-shaped in profile, with a broad, flat bottom. Projecting spurs are truncated, and the walls are smoothed and straightened. Tributary valleys, perhaps because they are occupied only by smaller glaciers or none at all, are usually unable to deepen as rapidly as the main valley and so become suspended above the main level; known as *hanging valleys,* these are often the later sites of spectacular waterfalls. A tidewater glacier can erode its valley floor below sea level; when it melts away, a steep-walled trough-like arm of the sea called a *fiord* results.

EXAMPLES: The magnificent Yosemite Falls in California plunges from a hanging valley into the glaciated valley of the Merced River. Fiords are especially well developed along the coast of Norway.

Valley-Floor Erosion. The floor of a glaciated valley tends to be irregular, since ice erodes more readily in fractured or weak rock than elsewhere; giant steps (called *cyclopean stairs, riegels,* and other names) are formed by this differential erosion at intervals along the length of the valley. In like manner, rock basins are carved in the valley floor and are sometimes strung out as a series of lakes called, because they are arranged like beads, *paternoster lakes.* The plasticity of ice enables it to override obstructions that a stream would have to cut through. Rounded humps of rocks, steep and rough on the leeward side, and known as *roches moutonnées,* or "sheep rocks," are modeled by the slow movement of a glacier over protruding knobs of bedrock. Abundant scratches and grooves made on the valley floor by the abrading action of rocks frozen into the base of the glacier are further evidence of past glaciation.

Ice-Sheet Erosion. Because continental glaciers are so much

U. S. Geological Survey   *Huff*

FIG. 29—Glaciated valley. Red Mountain Pass, Colorado.

more massive than valley glaciers (present ones in Greenland are as thick as 11,500 feet), the effects of their grinding action are far more pronounced. Roches moutonnées are more numerous, the grooving of bedrock is more conspicuous, and over vast areas the soil and mantle rock have been completely stripped away. The direction from which the glaciers came can be traced for hundreds of miles by the scratches left on freshly exposed rock; these scratches are made, as has been mentioned, not by the ice itself, but by rocks carried along by the ice. The regional relief is increased substantially where glaciers have moved parallel to the major streams and have deepened their valleys. Long, narrow lakes gouged out by the advancing glaciers are found in certain favored localities.

EXAMPLES: The deep glacial scouring on Kelleys Island, in Lake Erie, and the Finger Lakes of central New York are classic examples of the effects of ice-sheet erosion.

GLACIAL TRANSPORTATION

The rock fragments carried by a glacier are sometimes very large, because the strength of a glacier is sufficient to transport enormous boulders with the same ease that it carries small particles and a huge amount of so-called *rock flour*—all of which constitute the glacier's *load*. In an active glacier this material always moves forward, even though the end of the glacier is receding because of warmer temperatures.

Rocks frozen within the body of a glacier make up the *englacial drift*. Boulders carried on the surface of a glacier may protect the ice beneath from melting in the sun, and hence, a pinnacle of ice called an *ice pedestal,* capped by a *glacier table,* may persist. Heated rocks and dust piles, on the contrary, may sink into the surface ice, forming depressions called *dust wells.* Also transported on the glacier are vertical pits known as *moulins,* or *glacier mills,* which are crevasses rounded and enlarged by meltwater descending from the surface in warm weather.

The *zone of accumulation,* in the headward portion of a glacier, has its counterpart in the *zone of wastage,* at the foot. The wastage consists of melting and evaporation (together called *ablation*) and the *calving* of icebergs which float off to sea. Considerable material is added to glaciers, even in the zone of wastage, by avalanches, tributary glaciers, volcanic deposition, and the wind.

GLACIAL DEPOSITION

As a reminder of the time when all such deposits were thought to have drifted in by water or on floating ice, presumably during the Biblical Flood, the term *glacial drift* applies to all the rock material transported and deposited by glaciers. *Till* is haphazardly accumulated drift, with little semblance of sorting or layering (which require the influence of water). After the ice melts, part of the glacial material is reworked by meltwater streams, and some is carried into bodies of standing water.

Moraines. Drift that has been laid down in a fairly regular (usually linear) pattern and makes a recognizable land form is called a *moraine*. The types of moraine are named according to their position in relation to the glacier.

Ground Moraines. A glacier overloaded at the base may drop some of its rock along the floor and move over it. Upon retreating, it leaves additional rock waste, usually incased in a matrix of sandy clay known as *boulder clay*. This irregularly scattered debris constitutes the *ground moraine*. A continental glacier produces one of immense size. A large glacial boulder that is foreign to the rock upon which it rests is an *erratic;* some of these boulders have traveled long distances. A series of erratics from the same source, spread out from the place of origin, form a *boulder train*.

EXAMPLE: Erratics of native copper torn from the rocks of northern Michigan have been found distributed from Iowa to Ohio.

The ground moraine of a continental glacier is characterized by an irregular topography, poorly drained. It is marked in places by clusters of small oval hills called *drumlins,* which show a gentle slope in the direction of ice movement and a steeper slope facing the oncoming glacier.

EXAMPLE: The hills and islands in and near Boston, Massachusetts, are typical drumlins.

End Moraines. An end moraine is a curving ridge of drift formed at the front margin of a melting glacier which has halted

long enough for till to accumulate. Parallel morainal lobes indicate a fluctuation in the standing position of the ice. A *recessional
moraine* is a similar deposit left by a retreating glacier. A *terminal
moraine* is the end moraine of a valley glacier. The irregular surface of the complex end zone of a continental glacier is referred
to as *hummocky* or *knob and kettle* topography, having alternate
hills and hollows.

EXAMPLE: The prominent Ronkonkoma (outer) and Harbor Hill
(inner) ridges of Long Island, New York, are recessional moraines.

LATERAL MORAINES. The sides of a valley glacier are outlined
by ridges of rock debris torn from the valley walls and fallen
from the cliffs above. These are *lateral moraines,* and they grade
into the terminal moraine at the foot of the glacier. When two
valley glaciers unite in a single stream of ice, adjacent lateral
moraines join in a central dark streak, a *medial moraine.*

Glaciofluvial Deposits. Unlike till, which is deposited from a
glacier without the aid of running water, *glaciofluvial* (or *glacio-
fluviatile*) *deposits* are sorted and layered· by the movements of
glacial streams. No sharp demarcation exists between the deposits
due entirely to ice and those due in part to the action of flowing
water.

KAMES. Low, irregularly conical mounds of roughly layered
glacial sand and gravel are called *kames;* they often occur in
clusters. They are associated with the end-moraine area of both
valley and continental glaciers, but there is no agreed-upon
theory as to their origin. Some doubtless represent fillings of
openings in stagnant ice; others may have formed where the
glacial stream escaped from the ice. Glaciofluvial deposits left by
streams between the sides of a shrinking glacier and the enclosing
walls of the valley are known as *kame terraces.* These stand above
the valley after the ice has disappeared.

CREVASSE-FILLING. Straight, steep ridges of fine and coarse glacial material have been found extending as much as a mile in
length. These are believed to represent the partial filling, by the
action of flowing meltwater, of crevasses in the stagnant ice of a
continental glacier.

ESKERS. Narrow, winding ridges of poorly sorted and layered
sand and gravel, found in areas once occupied by the ground
moraine of a continental glacier, are known as *eskers.* They often

run for miles, though usually not continuously, and may branch. Eskers are believed to be deposits laid down by streams flowing through tunnels within or beneath the ice of a wasting glacier. At the margin of a glacial lake, they may take the form of deltas.

OUTWASH DEPOSITS. In contrast to the above-mentioned ice-

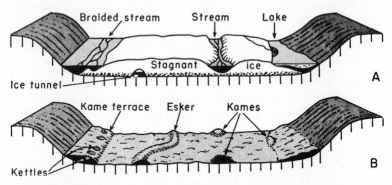

FIG. 30—Origin of bodies of ice-contact stratified drift. (By permission from *Glacial and Pleistocene Geology*, by Richard F. Flint, copyright, 1957, John Wiley and Sons, Inc., New York.)

contact features are those deposits, known as *proglacial deposits,* made beyond the limits of the glacier itself. The sediment carried forward from the margin of a glacier by the meltwater is termed *outwash.* Streams issuing from the ice are heavily loaded with sediment and have a milky appearance. They deposit rapidly in a complex braided pattern of channels. Beyond the end moraine of a continental glacier the sediment is spread out in a series of alluvial fans, which coalesce into a broad *outwash plain.* Though sometimes remarkably flat, in other places this plain is pockmarked by pits called *kettles,* which result from the melting of large isolated blocks of ice left behind during the recession of the main body of the glacier. This kind of outwash plain is referred to as a *pitted plain.* The outwash deposit of a valley glacier is called a *valley train;* it may actually extend far beyond the end of the particular valley.

Glacial-Lake Deposits. Stream-transported glacial sediment is deposited in temporary small lakes occupying kettles on the outwash plain of a glacier, depressions between the end of a receding glacier and the terminal moraine, and valleys blocked by moraines of any type. Where the land is high in front of a stationary or retreating glacier, the melting ice may be trapped and form a huge marginal glacial lake, until eventually an outlet is cut across the lowest point in the divide and the lake is drained, leaving thick accumulations of sediment. Some of these deposits are of the periodic variety known as *varves* (see p. 142).

EXAMPLE: Lake Winnipeg, Lake Manitoba, and Lake of the Woods (in Canada) are remnants of glacial Lake Agassiz (larger than all the present Great Lakes), which resulted from the damming of the northeast drainage of this region while the ice still filled the Hudson Bay area.

REVIEW QUESTIONS

1. State the possible causes of glaciation.
2. How is snow transformed into crystalline ice?
3. How do glaciers advance and recede?
4. Name the three main kinds of glaciers and tell where each is located.
5. Explain the processes of glacial erosion.
6. Why does the load of a glacier vary in size and composition?
7. Sketch a glacier and indicate the positions of the several types of moraines.
8. How does an esker differ from a kame?
9. Where do glacial-lake deposits occur?
10. Compare and contrast the movement of a stream and a glacier.

14
Swamps and Lakes

Swamps and lakes are widespread topographic features. They may mark successive stages toward the inundation of the land by bodies of water, or they may represent the reverse process, the drying up of a watery region. Most swamps represent a phase intermediate between lakes and dry land. Many a shallow basin contains either a swamp or a lake, according to the season. Swamps originate in several ways, and lakes, in numerous ways.

SWAMPS

A swamp is a low area of wet, soggy ground usually filled with a spongy mass of decaying vegetation and often covered by plants adapted to that environment. It may contain fresh, brackish, or salt water, and may occur even in a desert, though characteristically it is found in a moist region. The humus soil in swamps is referred to as *muck*. Forests of large trees grow in certain swamps.

Kinds of Swamps. A swamp is often called a *bog, peat bog,* or *marsh.* The vegetation of these types of swamps consists of low forms such as grass, moss, and lichen.

Peat Bogs. Sphagnum moss is the typical plant of peat bogs, making up probably 80 per cent of the substrate (underlying material). It commences growth on the border of a lake and extends gradually into the middle, where death, partial decay, and burial convert it to peat (the first step in the creation of coal).

Tidal Marshes. Along the coast, where shallow bays and lagoons are alternately submerged and abandoned by the tides, tidal marshes occur. They stay wet during the period of low tide, and the vegetation is composed of salt-water grasses.

Muskegs. Large, flat, and poorly drained areas of the north are covered by a black soil, rich in decayed vegetation and saturated to varying degrees with water. These muskeg swamps, interspersed with areas of open water, are very difficult to traverse. These are essentially the same as peat bogs.

EXAMPLE: Muskegs extend over vast reaches of Canada and the north-central United States.

TUNDRA. North of the muskeg country the ground is permanently frozen at shallow depths. The spongy, waterlogged topography is that of the *tundra,* also known in North America as the "barrens" or "barren lands."

EXAMPLE: Tundra is widely developed in the Arctic regions of Canada and Siberia.

Occurrence of Swamps. Three types of terrain are especially favorable for the existence of swamps: (1) undrained glaciated areas; (2) recently uplifted coastal plains; (3) floodplains and deltas of streams.

EXAMPLES: (1) The swamps of the Great Lakes region and the peat bogs of Ireland and the vast muskeg areas are remnants of the Ice Age. (2) The Everglades in Florida and the Dismal Swamp in Virginia and North Carolina were formerly part of the sea floor. (3) The lowland beyond the natural levees of the Lower Mississippi River is a series of swamps.

LAKES

Lakes are bodies of standing water ranging in size from small ponds to huge inland seas. They acquire their supply of water from flowing streams, from melting snow and glacial ice, from underground seepage and springs, and directly from rain and snow. Lakes with well-defined inlets and outlets have definite currents, which may also be caused by prevailing winds. Most lakes intersect the water table, which provides a continuous supply of water, but small lakes may occur in perched water tables above the regular zone of saturation, or in shallow basins that receive frequent additions of water.

All lakes are temporary features of the landscape, ultimately to be drained or filled with soil. Lakes act as settling basins for sediment removed from the land; they moderate the climate and increase rainfall; they regulate the volume of stream discharge, reducing extremes both of floods and of low water; and they conserve water that serves for drinking, irrigation, and power.

Origin of Lakes. What we are really concerned with here is the origin of lake basins, which are produced by a wide variety of geologic activities. Often more than one agent is involved. Depressions or obstructions to drainage channels which lead to lake formation occur in the following ways.

BY GLACIATION. Glaciation is responsible for the origin of more lakes than are all other causes combined. Innumerable lakes occur in recently glaciated parts of the Northern Hemisphere. They are found in scoured rock basins; in areas hemmed in by terminal, lateral, and ground moraines; in valleys blocked off by moraines; and in basins or valleys dammed by the ice itself.

EXAMPLE: The basins of the beautiful Finger Lakes of New York were gouged out below sea level by lobes of a continental glacier.

BY STREAMS. Many lakes are merely the wide portions of streams. Other lakes of stream origin are situated in plunge basins below waterfalls; in cut-off meanders (oxbow lakes); and in basins due to irregular deposition on floodplains and deltas or those behind alluvial fans, dams of driftwood, or dams of sediment deposited by overloaded tributaries.

EXAMPLES: Lake Pontchartrain, Louisiana, is a large example of a delta lake located in a subsiding area. The series of beautiful lakes at St. Moritz in Switzerland is due to damming of the main stream by deposition of alluvium brought in by tributary streams.

BY GROUND WATER. In the karst areas of the world, lakes are abundant, occupying sinks developed in carbonate and other soluble rocks.

EXAMPLE: More than 30 sink lakes are enclosed within the city limits of Orlando, Florida.

BY WAVES AND CURRENTS. Lagoons and bays can be converted into lakes by sand bars, which are the result of the action of waves and currents, aided by wind. The salt water may later be replaced by an inflow of fresh water from the land.

EXAMPLE: Numerous lakes along the Atlantic Coast from New York to Panama have this origin.

BY WIND. Basins excavated in soft rock by the wind may become the sites of small lakes. Lakes may also be found in depressions among sand dunes, and in streams and along the coast where drifting sand has impounded the water.

EXAMPLE: A number of lakes occur among the sand dunes of northern Indiana, near the south end of Lake Michigan.

BY GRAVITY. Landslides, mudflows, slumping, and mass wasting of all types may perform the work of blocking a stream valley to form a lake.

EXAMPLE: Lake San Cristobal, Colorado, came into being when the Slumgullion mudflow moved downhill six miles into a valley.

BY VULCANISM. Lakes are found in the craters and calderas of many extinct volcanoes, as well as on the irregular surfaces of laval flows. Molten lava may flow across a stream, blocking it and producing a lake.

EXAMPLE: Crater Lake, Oregon, occupying a caldera, is one of the scenic wonders of America.

BY DIASTROPHISM. Crustal movements bring into existence basins that may fill with water. The rise of a continental shelf exposes water-filled hollows in the newly established land. More pronounced uplift, such as that which makes mountains, leaves relatively down-folded areas as depressions, which may become lakes. Tilted fault blocks commonly provide lake basins. Larger ones lie in the down-dropped segment between parallel faults (grabens).

EXAMPLES: The Dead Sea, in Israel and Jordan, and the chain of great East African lakes such as Tanganyika and Nyasa are situated in the Great Rift Valley, a zone of faulted trenches, which also contain the River Jordan and the Red Sea.

BY METEORITES. The pits that result when large meteorites strike the earth may become filled with water.

EXAMPLE: Chubb Lake in northern Quebec occupies the largest known meteorite crater.

BY ORGANISMS. Some lakes of recent origin have been formed by the growth of vegetation around melting snow banks, by the activities of beavers and bison, and by the work of men. Man-made lakes may be very large; the others are comparatively small.

EXAMPLE: Man-made Lake Mead has a storage capacity of nearly 10 trillion gallons of Colorado River water.

Destruction of Lakes. The same geologic processes that create lakes constantly modify them and eventually destroy them, either by filling them with sediment or by draining them as their outlets are lowered by erosion. Filling helps to erode the outlet by raising the water level. Rivers, which widen to form many of the world's lakes, may destroy them, as they deepen their outlet valleys below the level of the lake basin. Some lakes vanish as a result of the disappearance of their water supply by (1) the diversion of the streams that feed them, (2) excess evaporation from their surface, or (3) leakage from below. Glacier-dammed lakes disappear with the melting of the ice.

EXAMPLES: Alachua Lake, formed in 1871 in a sink in Florida, drained underground when the clogged outlet was again naturally opened. Lake Agassiz disappeared when the ice melted out of the Hudson Bay area.

BY DELTAS. The principal way in which lakes become filled with sediment is by the deposition of deltas. Lake deltas resemble the deltas formed by streams as they enter the ocean, but are often more symmetrically fan-shaped.

EXAMPLE: The delta of the Rhone River is now 20 miles long and is filling Lake Geneva.

BY VARVED CLAYS. Lakes at the forward margins of glaciers are especially subject to rapid filling by varved * clays deposited by the melting ice. Advancing glaciers obliterate previously existing lakes.

BY ORGANIC MATERIAL. Vegetation helps to fill many small lakes, changing them into swamps as it accumulates and traps sediment carried into it. The accumulation of plant debris and the skeletal or shell remains of animals which settle on the bottom also aid in this filling. Fresh-water marls and diatomaceous earth deposits belong in this category.

BY SAND AND ASH. Wind-blown sand and migrating dunes sometimes destroy lakes by filling them. During volcanic eruption, ash may fall into a lake basin.

* A *varve* is a pair of annual layers of silt deposited in a body of still water. A thin, fine-grained dark band is deposited during the winter and a thick, coarser, light-colored band during the summer.

EXAMPLE: Prehistoric Lake Florissant in Colorado was completely filled with volcanic ash, which has preserved fishes, twigs, and about half of all the fossil butterflies ever discovered.

BY OTHER AGENTS. Wave erosion, landslides and other gravity movements, warping, and laval flows are among the other means by which the life of a lake is terminated.

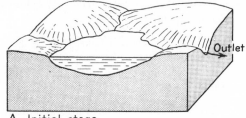

A. Initial stage.

Saline Lakes. The water of a mountain lake in a humid region is only slightly mineralized, since there is little loss by evaporation, whereas lakes in an arid region, with no outlets, lose their water almost entirely by evaporation. Eventually they become so rich in dissolved salts that these are precipitated out of the saturated solution. The kind of salt that will deposit is determined by the composition of the rocks through which the streams and ground water move to the

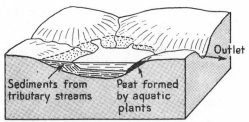

B. Lake basin partially filled by sediments and peat.

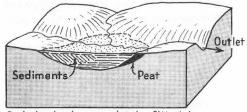

C. Lake basin completely filled by sediments and peat.

FIG. 31—Destruction of a lake as a temporary landform. (L. Don Leet and Sheldon Judson, *Physical Geology*, 2nd ed., 1958 by Prentice-Hall, Inc., Englewood Cliffs, New Jersey. Reproduced by permission of the publisher.)

lake basin. Lakes that were formerly part of the ocean have a head start in this process of concentrating chemical compounds by evaporation.

EXAMPLE: The Caspian Sea, the largest inland bed of salt water (much less salty than the ocean), was cut off from the ocean by the rise of the intervening land. Its present salt-water content is due largely, however, to extreme evaporation of the fresh water of the Volga River and other streams that enter it.

Ordinary *salt lakes* have a predominance of sodium chloride (common salt).

EXAMPLE: Great Salt Lake, Utah, is the shrunken remnant of ancient Lake Bonneville, which formerly covered about one-third of Utah. In the Pleistocene, when it stood at its highest level, it had an outlet to the Columbia River.

Alkaline lakes contain a large amount of potassium or sodium carbonate.

EXAMPLE: Mono Lake, California, is one of many once larger lakes in the Basin and Range province of the United States.

Beds of potash and borax constitute important mineral resources in some saline lakes.

EXAMPLE: Searles Lake, California, yields vast tonnages of borax, potash, and sodium salts.

Desert lakes that expand and contract seasonally may spread over a large area in a short while because their basins are so shallow. When dry, their silty surfaces become coated with salt. Such an ephemeral lake is called a *playa* (beach), or *playa lake*.

EXAMPLE: Death Valley, California, contains a number of playas.

REVIEW QUESTIONS

1. Describe muskegs and tundra.
2. What three terrains favor the presence of swamps?
3. How may a lake exist above the water table?
4. How do glaciers form lakes?
5. Name six kinds of lake basins.
6. How are lakes filled?
7. What causes a playa?
8. Define a swamp.
9. Explain the origin of a dead sea.

15
Oceans

Covering 71 per cent of the surface of our planet are the several connected oceanic bodies and their outlying gulfs, bays, and similar areas—collectively called the *sea*. Biologists believe that the sea was the original home of life. As a determiner of geologic, climatic, and economic conditions, the sea is of profound significance in the life of mankind. It is the primary source of the water that nourishes plants and animals, the regulator of climates, the globe-encircling route of commerce, a bountiful supplier of food, and the ultimate resting place of the material removed from the land by the forces of erosion set in motion by the evaporation of sea water. The oceans constitute a world in themselves, complementary to the less extensive world of the land. Within their depths is a teeming life surpassing anything known above water. On the bottom of the sea are impressive mountain ranges, lofty volcanic peaks, and enormous troughs and canyons.

Acting like a vast lake without an outlet, the ocean serves to concentrate mineral matter acquired from the land. The dissolved salts total 3.44 per cent, of which 77.76 per cent is sodium chloride. Marine organisms remove other compounds, chiefly calcium carbonate and silica, as part of their life processes. Other mineral matter precipitates when the temperature rises (driving off carbon dioxide) or when evaporation is excessive, as in closed basins and shallow inlets.

SUBMARINE TOPOGRAPHY

The great depressed portions of the earth's surface, lying between the elevated continental masses, are known as the *ocean basins*. The water that fills them overflows the rim of the continents and periodically invades the low-lying heart of even the largest land bodies. If the continents did not continue to rise, the ocean would soon overwhelm everything (the average depth of the ocean is about 12,500 feet, while the average elevation of the land is about 2,700 feet).

Going from the edge of the land to the middle of the sea, one crosses the following zones, each with its characteristic life.

1. The *littoral,* or *tidal, zone* includes the strip of land bared between high and low tides. *Mean sea level,* the reference plane used for all mapping purposes, is based upon the mid-altitude of this zone. Owing to the strong wave action, tidal-zone organisms must burrow into the mud or attach themselves to something firm in order to survive.

2. The upper level of the open ocean beyond the littoral zone, rich in floating and free-swimming forms of life, is known as the *pelagic zone.*

3. The *continental shelf* is the margin of the land submerged under shallow water. It slopes seaward to a maximum depth of about 600 feet, and its extremely abundant life belongs to the *neritic zone.* This is the environment that prevailed from time to time in the geologic past when shallow inland seas covered larger areas of the continents.

4. Beyond the continental shelf, the sea bottom drops away more abruptly to form the *continental slope,* extending between 600 and 6,000 feet in depth. The corresponding life zone is called the *bathyal zone;* few plants but many animals are present.

5. The ocean basin, below 6,000 feet, is represented by the *abyssal zone,* containing only organisms adapted to life in the dark depths under terrific pressures.

The bottom of the sea is highly diversified. It contains long mountain ranges and ridges; volcanic cones singly, in groups, and in rows; plateaus; plains; oval and elongated basins; canyons and gorges; and other features as varied as those seen on land.

Sea Mounts. Underwater mountains known as *sea mounts* are common in certain areas. Flat-topped sea mounts, called *guyots* (after the Swiss geologist Arnold Guyot), may be volcanic peaks once truncated by wave erosion and since subsided to a depth of several thousand feet, or may form with flat tops under water.

EXAMPLE: Sea mounts are numerous in the Gulf of Alaska, and guyots between the Hawaiian and Mariana Islands.

Deeps. A *deep* is any depression below 6,000 meters (19,685 feet). The greatest deeps are the *trenches* (sometimes 1,500 miles or more long), which may be due to faulting or pronounced down-folding. They occur at the foot of continental slopes and coincide with major submarine earthquake belts. The origin of these trenches is not fully understood.

EXAMPLE: The Marianas Trench (east of the Philippines, between the islands of Guam and Yap) contains the deepest known spot on earth, under 36,560 feet of water.

Submarine Canyons. Among the unsolved mysteries of ocean topography are the *submarine canyons*. They cross the continental shelf and continental slope in many places like youthful stream valleys, some having tributaries with a dendritic pattern. Although some are continuations of present-day rivers, others are not. Numerous explanations have been advanced to account for them. Perhaps the most favored hypotheses involve (1) bottom *turbidity currents* of suspended mud and (2) stream erosion in coastal mountainous terrain (while the sea level was lowered during the Ice Age).

EXAMPLES: The Hudson River continues seaward 150 miles in a submarine canyon. The submarine canyon of the Congo River is also outstanding.

MARINE SEDIMENTS

The sediments found on the floor of the sea, intimately mixed in their occurrence, come from four sources:

1. Land-derived (*terrigenous*) sediment, contributed by streams, coastal erosion, volcanoes, wind, and floating ice.

2. Marine (*pelagic*) sediment, the skeletons and shells of plants and animals.

3. Submarine volcanic ash.

4. Meteoritic material.

Classification. According to their composition, marine sediments are classified as follows:

1. Clay, silt, and sand on continental shelves and continental slopes.

2. *Calcareous ooze* (more than 30 per cent calcium carbonate) in relatively shallow warm water. *Globigerina ooze* and *pteropod*

ooze are common types consisting of accumulations of the skeletons of these microscopic organisms.

3. Red clay (less than 30 per cent calcium carbonate) in cool or deep water.

4. *Siliceous ooze,* mostly in very deep or cold water. *Radiolarian ooze* and *diatomaceous ooze* are common types made up respectively of the siliceous skeletal remains of microscopic animals (radiolarians) or plants (diatoms).

Coral Reefs. No aspect of marine geology has been the subject of more speculation by geologists than have coral reefs. Though they receive their name from the conspicuous presence of colonies of corals, the predominant portion of the reefs is constructed by other lime-secreting organisms, both plant and animal. A *fringing reef* is a massive belt of such skeletal material built along the shore. When separated from the shore by a lagoon or channel, it is termed a *barrier reef.* A nearly circular one with a lagoon in the center is called an *atoll.* A fringing reef that surrounds a sinking island will continue to build upward, changing successively into a barrier reef, an atoll, and (by filling) a round coral island. Atolls may also have originated by the growth of coral reefs on top of volcanic islands that were cut down by waves when the sea level was lowered during the Ice Age.

EXAMPLE: The Great Barrier Reef, the world's largest coral reef, varies from 10 to 90 miles in width and stretches more than 1,000 miles along the northeast coast of Australia.

MOVEMENT OF SEA WATER

The ceaseless motion of the sea is extremely complex. It is a result of the earth's rotation, the tides, the wind, precipitation, evaporation, the varying temperature, salinity, and density of the water, earthquakes, subsurface gravity movements, the flow of water from the land, the configuration of the shore, and still other factors, all closely related in their effects. The most regular and predictable movement of sea water is produced by the tides, and the most sudden and unpredictable movements are caused by tsunamis (so-called tidal waves, due to earthquakes) and by storms.

Tides. Under normal circumstances the sea rises and falls twice during a period of 24 hours and 51 minutes (the interval between successive high tides averaging 12 hours, 25.5 minutes). The tides are the resultant of the gravitational attraction of the sun and moon (especially the latter), combined with the centrifugal force caused by the rotation of the earth, and modified by the contour of the shore, the topography of the land, and the vagaries of the wind. The normal tide may be heightened where the water funnels through a narrow opening as a *bore,* or *tidal current.*

EXAMPLE: The tide in the Bay of Fundy, between Nova Scotia and New Brunswick, raises the water level as much as 70 feet.

Currents. The circulation of ocean currents is influenced by prevailing winds, equatorial heating and polar cooling, the rotation of the earth, and the shape of the land masses against which they touch. Unequal heating by the sun creates *thermal-circulation currents,* which, in turn, affect the climate of nearby lands. Surface currents generated by winds are called *wind-drift currents* and are very widespread. When the water strikes the coast at an angle, a *longshore current* parallel to the shoreline is produced.

EXAMPLES: The Gulf Stream and the Japan Current (east of Formosa and along the Japanese archipelago) are major thermal-circulation currents.

Waves. The oscillation of water particles in nearly circular orbits constitutes *wave motion.* Waves are relatively superficial, but when these "waves of oscillation" drag bottom in shallow water and "break" as *surf* or "waves of translation" they may have considerable energy. The backwash creates *rip currents* on the surface and *undertow.*

EXAMPLE: Windows in a lighthouse at Dunnet Head, Scotland, have been broken 300 feet above sea level by wave-thrown stones.

SHORE EROSION

The seacoast is worn away by a combination of processes, as follows:

1. Impact of waves upon loose material.

2. *Hydraulic plucking,* or *quarrying,* of blocks of rock by the pressure of waves against the air contained within cracks in the coastal wall.

3. Abrasion by rock fragments hurled by waves.

4. Scouring by currents moving along the bottom.

5. Solution by water, especially in limestone formations, such as coral.

Undercutting by the surf produces a cliff called a *sea cliff* or *wave-cut cliff*, often notched at the base to become a *sea cave*. If the roof of the cave is broken through, the water is forced upward as a *spouting horn*. As the cliff slowly retreats under continued erosion, a flat surface sloping toward the sea and known as a *wave-cut terrace* or *wave-cut bench* is planed away, leaving grooves, tidal pools, resistant "rock reefs," and other irregularities to indicate its origin. Isolated vertical projections of rock remaining when the surrounding land is planed down are known as *sea stacks;* some of them have been pierced to become *natural bridges* or arches.

EXAMPLES: The beautiful Blue Grotto on the island of Capri, in the Bay of Naples, is a sea cave. One of the most photographed sea stacks is the Old Man of Hoy, found off the Orkney Islands, on the north coast of Scotland. A widely visited offshore natural bridge is the pierced rock at Percé on the Gaspé Peninsula, Quebec.

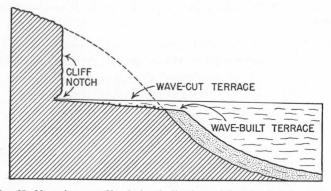

FIG. 32—Near-shore profile, dashes indicating original land surface. (By permission from *Geology*, by von Engeln and Caster. Copyright, 1952. McGraw-Hill Book Co., Inc.)

SHORE TRANSPORTATION

Rock material eroded from the coast is carried seaward, chiefly by currents and the undertow of breaking waves. Some of it is temporarily deposited by the action of waves below the sea cliff on the wave-cut terrace; the portion that is visible above sea level constitutes the *beach*. The beach is alternately widened and narrowed during times of calm and storm, respectively, and its material drifts along the shore, sometimes for long distances. Beyond the wave-cut terrace is a larger aggregation of sediment in transit, extending outward an indefinite distance. During movement the rock particles are worn, rounded, and sorted.

SHORE DEPOSITION

The eroded shore material is deposited when waves and currents lose some of their carrying power. In addition, a major contribution to beach deposits is made by streams discharging along the shoreline. *Pocket beaches* have accumulated in small indentations, and *bayhead beaches* in larger openings along the coast. The principal mineral constituent of sand is quartz, but sands of other kinds are not rare. Beach pebbles may be flattened into disk-shaped pieces which overlap to form a *shingle beach*.

Offshore from many beaches are two or more low parallel submarine ridges of sand, with shallow troughs between; they are termed *longshore bars* and are built up by breaking waves. Offshore from some gently sloping sandy beaches a single ridge forms a strip of land exposed above water, called a *barrier beach* or *barrier island;* it is parallel to the mainland (from which it is separated by a lagoon). This feature is also known as an *offshore bar* or *island bar,* another of a number of types of bars or barriers, each named from its situation with respect to the land. Thus, a *baymouth bar,* or *bar barrier,* almost or entirely blocks the entrance to a bay. A bar that continues out into open water from a beach and is shaped by longshore currents is termed a *spit;* it may be deflected as a *recurved spit* or *hook,* or even double back to the mainland again as a *loop.* Bars may extend until they connect with islands, which are then referred to as *tied islands,* the connecting bar being called a *tombolo.*

EXAMPLES: Coney Island and Jones Beach, recreational centers of New York City, are barrier beaches, as are the resorts of Atlantic City, New Jersey, and Daytona Beach, Palm Beach, and Miami Beach, Florida. The tip of Cape Cod at Provincetown, Massachusetts, is an ideally formed spit recurved, as is Sandy Hook at the entrance to New York

Harbor. The Rock of Gibraltar is an island tied to the coast of Spain by a tombolo.

SHORELINE DEVELOPMENT

Geologists have recognized four types of shorelines:

1. *Shoreline of emergence,* formed by the rise of land above sea level. A wide coastal plain covered with marine sediments; often with wave-cut terraces on land and usually with barrier beaches offshore.

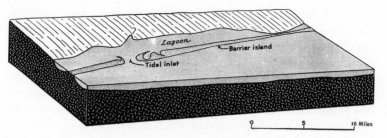

Fɪɢ. 33—Features of deposition along regular shoreline. (L. Don Leet and Sheldon Judson, *Physical Geology,* 1954 by Prentice-Hall, Inc., Englewood Cliffs, New Jersey. Reproduced by permission of the publisher.)

2. *Shoreline of submergence,* formed by the sinking of land below sea level. Usually very irregular, with rocky headlands, deep coves, islands, and drowned valleys.

3. *Neutral shoreline,* formed by volcanic activity, coral reefs, faulting, excess sedimentation from inland. Not due to marine erosion.

4. *Compound shoreline,* combining two or three of the above types.

Owing to repeated changes in sea level during the Ice Age, as well as to warping of the land, it is difficult to trace in an actual coastal area the evolution of any of the preceding types of shoreline through their normal stages of youth, maturity, and old age, corresponding to the cycle in other landscapes. Frequent interruptions have superimposed one set of features upon another, so that these arbitrary classifications are generally not satisfactory.

REVIEW QUESTIONS

1. Why are oceans important geologically?
2. Draw a profile showing the principal marine zones.

3. Describe the life in each of the zones.
4. Give two possible explanations for the origin of submarine canyons.
5. What are the sources of marine sediments?
6. Name the kinds of marine sediments.
7. What is the possible sequence of events in the development of coral reefs?
8. What is a barrier reef? An atoll?
9. How is shore erosion accomplished?
10. Describe these erosional features of a seacoast: sea cliff, sea cave, wave-cut terrace, sea stack.
11. Describe these depositional features of a seacoast: beach, longshore bar, barrier island, spit.
12. How can an offshore island become part of the mainland without a change in sea level?

16
Wind

Wind is the atmosphere in motion. It is an agent of erosion, transportation, and deposition; but its geologic effects are everywhere subordinate to those of running water. Wind is, of course, more effective in arid regions than in moist climates.

About one-sixth of the land area of the earth is desert, lying either in subtropical belts of high atmospheric pressure or on the leeward side of high mountain ranges. A desert region is often characterized by interior drainage, angularity of topography, and barrenness of landscape. The precipitation is not adequate to support a thorough growth of vegetation and the rains are sporadic, brief, and violent—factors that prevent the maintenance of a soil cover. Despite popular belief, sand and gravel cover only small portions of the great desert areas; but they furnish the tools with which the wind, energized by the sun, does its work.

WIND EROSION

The wind effects erosion in the following ways:

Deflation. Loose earth and small particles of rock are lifted up and carried away by the wind, a process known as *deflation*. *Blowouts* are basins excavated by wind in soft unconsolidated or poorly cemented materials. When the wind removes the finer sand and clay and leaves the larger rock pebbles behind as *lag gravel*, a coarse layer resembling a cobblestone road and called *desert pavement* may be produced.

The principal sources of the material eroded by deflation are beaches, the bottoms of playas and other dry lakes, floodplains and dry stream beds, glacial outwash plains, sand dunes, disintegrating sandstones, and volcanic ash deposits.

Abrasion. This process, also called *corrasion*, involves a sandblasting effect: the sand pits, etches, grooves, and scours exposed rock faces. Abrasion is most effective within an area about two feet from the ground, where most of the coarser particles of sand are carried.

Beveled stones called *ventifacts* are a common result of wind abrasion; they show a glossy luster and numerous tiny irregularities on their curved surfaces. Such stones often have a single well-defined edge and are referred to as *einkanter* (single-edge); those with three edges are *dreikanter;* but ventifacts may have many more small edges and facets.

WIND TRANSPORTATION

Air moves across the surface of the ground with *turbulent flow,* rising as it does so. Wind-blown sand travels as a low blanket, usually not more than three feet in height, with the bulk of the sand concentrated within the lower few inches. Individual particles of sand move by successive leaps referred to as *saltation.* The impact of grains of sand as they settle starts other grains into similar motion. The rest of the moving sand travels forward along the ground by *traction* (rolling and sliding) as the *bed load.*

The finer particles are swept upward for a distance of hundreds or thousands of feet, becoming a dust cloud held aloft in suspension (as the *suspended load*) by eddying currents of air.

EXAMPLE: Yellow silt from the interior of China often drops onto ships in the coastal waters of Japan, 1,000 miles away.

WIND DEPOSITION

As the wind loses its carrying power, or as rain washes through it, the sand and dust are deposited. Apart from the occasional fall of volcanic ash and the continuous fall of dust everywhere on earth, two distinctive kinds of *aeolian* (wind-blown) deposits are readily recognized.

Dunes. Any barrier that obstructs the wind will cause the accumulation of dunes. A *sand dune* may range from a few feet in height to hills several hundred feet high. As new material is added to the ripple-marked windward side, it is carried to the crest, from which it slides or rolls down the steeper lee slope, which finally slumps under gravity. After the dune has ceased to enlarge, it may continue, under favorable conditions, to build upward and forward in the same manner, so that the entire dune

moves, or *migrates,* in the direction of the wind. Where vegetation can get a foothold, however, it is effective in reducing or pre-
venting movement, and eventually a dune that fails to grow loses
volume or becomes a vegetation-covered *fixed dune.*

U. S. Geological Survey   *Balsley*

Fɪɢ. 34—Sand dunes. Imperial Valley, California.

The usual concentration of beach sand in a narrow strip along
the shore results in the development of ridges called *fore dunes,*
parallel to the shoreline. These may move inland to become
transverse dunes (athwart the onshore winds), a common type
which is also found outside coastal areas—such as the edge of a
lake or stream or the floor of a desert—wherever the wind blows
across a copious supply of loose sand.

The constancy of direction and the velocity of the prevailing
wind are responsible for the formation of three other dune types.
A steady wind blowing from only one direction fashions crescent-
shaped *barchan dunes,* occurring usually in clusters or in an offset
(*en echelon*) row; the horns of the crescent point with the wind
and surround the steep leeward side of the dune. Pointing in the
opposite direction are long scoop-shaped dunes called *parabolic*

dunes, which perhaps originate from the deflation holes known as blowouts. A gentle prevailing wind from one direction and an occasional stronger wind from another direction produce *longitudinal,* or *seif, dunes,* shaped like scimitars and occurring mostly in long rows, sometimes of great length.

Loess. Wind-blown silt carpets vast areas of certain parts of the world and constitutes a characteristic deposit referred to as *loess.* It covers hills and valleys alike and consists of fresh mineral particles, which yield a fertile yellowish soil. It lacks the layering generally associated with sedimentary deposits, but coheres so as to form steep, even vertical, cliffs. Loess has been transported by the wind from regions of glacial outwash and from deserts.

EXAMPLES: Loess hundreds of feet thick in China was transported from the Gobi Desert. Nearly a quarter million square miles of the Mississippi River Basin is covered with loess from the glaciated north-central states.

REVIEW QUESTIONS

1. What is wind?
2. Where do deserts occur?
3. What is deflation?
4. Explain the origin of desert pavement.
5. What is a ventifact?
6. How does wind move sediment?
7. Name five kinds of sand dunes.
8. What characterizes loess and where does it come from?

17
Maps

A *map* is a representation of the surface of the earth or some portion of it. It must show true distances and directions, or it remains merely a sketch and is not a map. In addition to the usual geographic maps familiar to the layman, the geologist uses two main kinds of maps, topographic and geologic.

Topographic maps show in detail the position, size, and shape of the physical features of a given area. The topography (representation of relief) is shown by contours or some other method on a *planimetric,* or *base, map,* which serves to fix the geographic locations.

Geologic maps show the kinds and attitudes of bedrock present throughout a given area, as well as the distribution of unconsolidated materials, alluvium, dunes, etc. The geologic data are overprinted on either topographic or planimetric maps, preferably the former. Structural features may be shown, as well as mineral deposits of economic value and other useful information capable of being mapped.

The five factors involved in map-making are projection, scale, orientation, conventional symbols, and topography.

Projection. It is impossible to represent the curved surface of the earth on flat pieces of paper without distortion. Systematic control of the amount and direction of the necessary distortion is accomplished by means of a system called *projection.* Projections may be made to show correctly the shapes of earth features (example: Mercator projection); to show areas in the proper ratios (example: Lambert's azimuthal projection); to preserve correctly the directions of all lines drawn from the center of the map (example: gnomonic projection); or they may be compromises between correct shapes, correct areas, and correct directions, to avoid too much exaggeration of any one aspect (example: polyconic projection).

Projections are actually mathematical devices, but the prin-

ciple underlying their use can be readily visualized by considering a simple example—the case of the cylindrical projection. Assume that a cylinder of paper is wrapped around a transparent
globe, touching at the equator. Imagine a point source of light
at the center of the globe which throws shadows or *projects* the
details on the surface of the globe (lines of latitude and longitude as well as the geographic outlines of the continents, etc.) onto
the cylinder. If these shadows or projections on the cylinder are
traced and the cylinder is then flattened out, one will have a map
of the world on a cylindrical projection. If, in place of a cylinder,
one uses a piece of paper in the form of a cone, with its axis co-
inciding with the axis of the earth, a map of one hemisphere will
be projected on a so-called conic projection.

Scale. The *scale* of a map is the proportion, or ratio, between
distance on the ground and the corresponding distance on the
map. Scale is indicated in three ways:

1. *Written scale,* stating proportionate measurement such as
"one inch equals one mile," meaning that one inch on the map
represents one mile on the ground.

2. *Graphic scale,* dividing a straight line into convenient units,
so that distance can be measured by comparison.

3. *Fractional scale,* stating the proportion by a "representative
fraction" (R.F.) such as 1:125,000, meaning that the actual geographic distance is 125,000 times as great as the corresponding
distance on the map. Most of the maps of the United States
Geological Survey use a scale of 1:24,000, 1:62,500, 1:125,000, or
1:250,000.

Orientation. The *orientation* of a map is its position with
respect to the four directions. Most topographic maps represent
four-sided units of area called *quadrangles.* True, or geographic,
north (pointing toward the North Pole) is at the top; the magnetic
North Pole does not coincide with the geographic North Pole,
and so a line pointing to it (as a compass needle points) rarely
coincides with the true-north line. The angle between the mag-
netic-north line and the true-north line is called the *magnetic
declination* and is usually indicated on the map sheet by means
of two arrows.

The east-west lines crossing the map horizontally are lines of
latitude, called *parallels of latitude,* which encircle the globe
parallel to the equator. Latitude is measured in degrees, minutes,

and seconds north and south from the equator; the United States and Canada are in north latitude. In the case of conic projections these lines are curved.

The north-south lines crossing the map vertically are lines of longitude, called *meridians of longitude,* which encircle the globe and come together at the North and South Poles. Because they converge slightly, a map bounded by them is not a true rectangle. Longitude is measured in degrees, minutes, and seconds east and west of the Prime Meridian, which goes through Greenwich, England. The United States and Canada are in west longitude.

Lines of latitude and longitude intersect to divide the earth into a grid system. Certain parallels of latitude are taken as *base lines,* certain meridians of longitude are taken as *principal meridians,* and units of land area are measured from them in a simple, essentially rectangular, system that is used throughout most of the interior and western part of the United States. This system was devised at the time of the opening up of the Northwest Territories in the upper Mississippi Valley in 1787. *Township lines* (T) are located at six-mile intervals north and south of each base line. *Range lines* (R) are laid off along each base line also at six-mile intervals. This would produce a square grid system, six miles on a side, except for the fact that north-south lines (meridians) converge toward the poles. Consequently, it is necessary to change base lines often if the *townships,* blocked out in this way, are to be approximately 36 square miles. Each township is divided into 36 *sections,* each with an area of approximately one square mile. A similar system is used in western Canada, but the sections are numbered in a different order.

Conventional Symbols. Water and ice features (*hydrography*) are shown in blue; works of man (*culture*) in black; and topography (*relief*) in brown. Main highways, towns not mapped in detail, and public-land survey lines are often shown in red. *Woodland* and other areas of vegetation may be overprinted in green. Dozens of symbols are in use for such features as sand dunes, dry lakes, railroad bridges, and county boundaries. On geologic maps such features as anticlines, faults, and joints, and different patterns for various kinds of rock are shown by appropriate symbols.

Topography. The configuration of the land is represented in several ways on topographic maps: by color, shading, *hachures* (short dashes running down slopes), and *contour lines.* Contour lines connect points that have the same *altitude* (elevation above sea level); by means of these lines the height and shape of the ground at any place can be determined. The *datum plane* is the surface from which all elevations on a map are measured; it is usually mean sea level, and the shoreline of the ocean may be regarded as the zero contour.

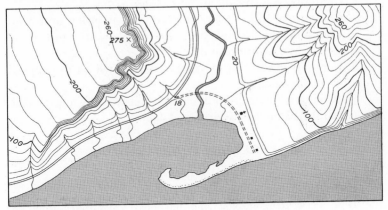

U.S. Geological Survey

Fig. 35—How landscape is shown on a topographic map.

Contour lines are usually drawn at certain regular intervals; the *contour interval* is the vertical difference in height between adjacent contour lines, and is usually 5, 10, 20, 40, 50, or 100 feet—the flatter the land, the smaller the interval needed to show details. Usually every fourth or fifth contour line *(index contour)* is heavier and its altitude is marked. Hollows are indicated by *depression contours,* which have added hachures pointing downslope. *Relief* is the difference in elevation between the tops of hills and the bottoms of valleys. Various individual elevations of importance are called *spot heights* or *spot elevations;* one permanently marked on the ground is called a *bench mark* (B.M.).

The following useful rules also apply to contour lines:

1. Contours separate all points of higher elevation than the contour from all points of lower elevation.

2. Contours are always continuous until they close, even though outside the limits of the map.

3. Contours never intersect or cross one another except at a very steep or overhanging cliff.

4. Closely spaced contours indicate steep slopes; widely spaced contours indicate flat land or gentle slopes; a change in spacing indicates a change in slope.

5. Contours are closer at the top of a concave slope and at the bottom of a convex slope.

6. Contours cross streams at right angles.

7. Contours bend in valleys and form a V pointing upstream.

8. Contours loop around spurs and ridges on hilly topography and form a U pointing downhill.

9. Contours on hills or in valleys are repeated on the opposite side of the hill or valley.

10. Contours in water bodies may be replaced by a generalized pattern that does not indicate actual depths.

REVIEW QUESTIONS

1. Name three kinds of maps and describe what each shows.
2. Why are map projections necessary?
3. How do written, graphic, and fractional scales differ from one another?
4. What causes magnetic declination?
5. Locate parallels of latitude and meridians of longitude on a map.
6. Draw a grid system and label: base lines, principal meridians, township lines, range lines, township, section.
7. How are the following shown on maps: hydrography, culture, relief, woodland, depressions?
8. What do contour lines signify?

PART II
Historical Geology

18
Origin of the Earth

Man has been speculating on the origin of the earth for thousands of years. His early speculations took the form of myth-making. Later, the ancient philosophers developed theories based on observation and reasoning. Truly scientific hypotheses had to wait until man had assembled adequate knowledge of the earth and its actual relation to the heavenly bodies.

None of the numerous hypotheses regarding the origin of the earth has been generally accepted because each hypothesis fails to account for certain facts which must be explained by any fully acceptable theory. Confronted by confusions and contradictions, as well as by the complex mathematics involved, the average geologist is tempted to consider this matter as one that does not directly concern his subject and to relegate it to the astronomers. Nevertheless, certain elaborate hypotheses of earth origin have played a significant role in the development of geologic theory, and for that reason are worthy of at least a brief consideration.

It seems most improbable that the earth (and its sister planets) originated in any fashion other than as an integral part of the solar system; and it is equally unthinkable for our solar system to have come into existence independently of the rest of the universe. More and more, calculations as to the age of all parts of the known cosmos seem to converge upon that remote hypothetical moment "when the world began."

THE NEBULAR HYPOTHESIS

Copernicus, Kepler, and Newton followed one another at intervals of about a century; another century later, based upon their profound discoveries, the first scientific hypothesis of earth origin was presented (in 1755) by the German metaphysician Immanuel Kant. This hypothesis was further developed in 1796 by the French mathematician and astronomer Pierre Simon de

Laplace, and was widely accepted during the nineteenth century.

The nebular hypothesis of Kant and Laplace is referred to as a *one-star hypothesis* because it explains the origin of the planets by the evolution of a single star, our sun, without the interference of any outside body.

The hypothesis postulates that a greatly diffused spherical cloud of gas, a nebula, extended outward at least to the present distance of the outermost planet. This cloud rotated slowly; as it cooled and contracted, its velocity around the sun increased, just as a whirling dancer spins faster as he draws his arms together. The gaseous mass gradually became a disk around the sun's equator. At critical points during this rotation, rings of fiery gas were assumed to have been thrown off by centrifugal force. Each ring then broke up and gathered into a sphere, producing a planet, which began to revolve around the sun in the same path as the former ring. A comparable process, operating in a minor way in the case of several of the planets, accounts for the formation of the satellites such as our moon. The earth-planet liquefied as it cooled, then with further cooling acquired a solid crust. The main body of the gas meanwhile condensed further to become the sun.

Among the more serious objections to the nebular hypothesis are the following:

1. The planets possess 98 per cent of the rotational energy of the solar system, whereas the sun has about 99.87 per cent of the mass.

2. The heavy elements in the earth can originate only at temperatures far higher than those prevailing on the sun.

3. Some of the satellites revolve in a retrograde (backward) direction, and one of them revolves faster than its planet rotates.

4. The mechanism of ring-formation does not correspond to the rotational velocity of a solar nebula as postulated.

THE PLANETESIMAL HYPOTHESIS

Finding nothing in outer space that corresponded to the nebula postulated by Kant and Laplace, and impressed by the recurrence of large-scale glaciation throughout geologic history, which seemed to contradict the idea of a steadily cooling earth, Thomas C. Chamberlin and Forest R. Moulton, an American geologist-astronomer team, presented the solar-disruption, or planetesimal, hypothesis in 1895. Geologists favored this conception of earth origin until about the time of World War II.

The planetesimal hypothesis of Chamberlin and Moulton is referred to as a *two-star hypothesis* because it explains the origin of the planets by a near collision between the sun and another star which disrupted it.

The hypothesis supposes that the world began with a sun nearly the same as the present one, ejecting material by internal explosions such as those seen today in the so-called solar prominences. The close passage of another star developed huge tidal bulges on two opposite sides of the sun, and the explosive force within drove them out in varying directions as great jets, or bolts, of gas. The attraction of the passing star drew these bolts into elliptical orbits around the sun. Five large bolts on the tidal bulge facing the sun broke up to form the major planets, and five smaller ones on the opposite side became the minor planets and asteroids, nearer the sun.

Some of the hot gas in the smaller bolts is presumed to have condensed rapidly into liquid and then cooled to solid particles, called *planetesimals* and resembling meteorites, revolving in swarms around the sun in a pattern like that of the many spiral nebulae seen in the sky. As their paths intersected, the nucleus of each planet was assembled, and these few grew by accretion to their present size, moving in more circular orbits as a result of the encounter. Thus the earth was solid from the start, except for a temporarily molten surface, which could result from heat generated by the rapid infall of planetesimals. The craters on the moon seem to show the effect of similar impacts.

Among the more serious objections to the planetesimal hypothesis are the following:

1. The concentric density layering of the earth indicates that it must once have been a molten body, which segregated into unlike zones, as slag does from molten metal.

2. The mechanism of solar eruption is inadequate to explain the tidal bulges.

3. A very rare and perhaps unique event in the universe is required.

4. The collision of planetesimals would more likely destroy than preserve them.

5. The amount of salt in the oceans, derived mostly from weathering of rock, is not enough for a slowly growing planet to have provided, considering all the time available for the process of erosion and deposition.

THE TIDAL HYPOTHESIS

Unconvinced that the earth has always been solid, James Jeans and Harold Jeffries, English astronomer and geophysicist, respectively, proposed in 1917 a gaseous two-star hypothesis. They theorized that another star closely approached the sun, producing tidal bulges, from which streamed an enormous cigar-shaped filament of solar gases. This incandescent filament was put into revolution around the sun. It then broke into segments which contracted into rotating spheres, the planets. Cooling from gas to liquid, one of these planets, Earth, gradually solidified to its present condition.

The objections to the tidal hypothesis are like many of those made to the planetesimal hypothesis, excluding the ones that are dependent upon an aggregation of originally solid material. The hypothesis explains most of the peculiarities of planet and satellite motion by complicated devices.

RECENT HYPOTHESES

With the development of new mathematical techniques and the discovery of new facts about the universe, the formulation of systems of earth origin is once again becoming fashionable among cosmogonists. Among those who have proposed new hypotheses are Berlage (1940), Alfvén (1942), von Weizsäcker (1945), Whipple (1947), ter Haar (1948), and Hoyle (1950). The general trend is apparently toward a modified version of the ancient nebular hypothesis, involving a vastly greater amount of very hot gaseous material flying from the sun by centrifugal force, a small portion of which condensed to form the planets.

The *dust-cloud hypothesis* of Fred L. Whipple suggests for the beginning of the earth a cloud of cosmic dust, similar to the many dark nebulae. This dust was driven together by the force of light on the outside, which, as we know, is able to propel the substance of comets. Moving streams of particles then separated into the planets and their satellites.

The *nova hypothesis* of Fred Hoyle and the older *binary-star hypothesis* (1936) of Henry N. Russell and R. A. Lyttleton involve double stars, or binaries, which are pairs revolving about a common center (about half the stars are probably of this type). Hoyle's view is that one member of the pair exploded to produce the material of the planets. Russell and Lyttleton favored tidal disruption of the companion star by the sun.

REVIEW QUESTIONS

1. Why does any theory of earth origin depend upon the facts of astronomy?
2. What scientists evolved the nebular hypothesis?
3. Summarize the nebular hypothesis.
4. State three objections to the nebular hypothesis.
5. Who devised the planetesimal hypothesis?
6. What is the planetesimal hypothesis?
7. State four objections to the planetesimal hypothesis.
8. What is the tidal hypothesis?
9. Describe two recent hypotheses of earth origin.

19

Evolution of Life

Geology deals not only with the nature and history of the earth itself, but also with the history of the plants and animals that have left their records in the rocks. *Fossils*—the remains and traces of the life of past ages—are as much an integral part of certain rocks as are the minerals, and the kinds of fossils found provide the chief means by which we date these rocks.

THE ORIGIN OF LIFE

The geologic evidence of past life consists of fossilized cellular structures representing once living organisms. Inasmuch as complex organic molecules are not stable under present conditions of temperature, light, and composition of the atmosphere and hydrosphere, only living matter can now synthesize organic compounds and thereby produce other living matter. This matter is based today principally on a small number of compounds—nucleic acids, proteins, carbohydrates, and fats.

If organic compounds originated in the past from inorganic matter (they cannot do so now) the environment then must have been deficient in oxygen, and especially deficient in ozone, in order to absorb ultraviolet radiation from the sun. Most free oxygen in the atmosphere appears to be of later biogenic origin, formed by the dissociation of carbon dioxide by plants. Between 1 billion and 2 billion years ago, the atmosphere is believed to have changed to one containing free oxygen, and the early ancestors of our present plant and animal life developed in consequence.

The hypothesis generally favored today is that life developed from nonliving matter. Organic substances are composed of the same chemical elements that exist in the inorganic world, and many organisms contain typically mineral structures. The border line between living and nonliving matter seems to be represented by *viruses*, which are chemical compounds too small to be

170

seen except with an electron microscope; they absorb nourishment, show adaptation, and reproduce themselves while in suitable media, but become inert crystals upon removal. The boundary between the plant and animal kingdoms is likewise vague, and the proper classification of certain one-celled organisms, such as slime molds, is disputed. In general, plants have no power of locomotion and tend to live attached or immobile; they manufacture their own food from the surrounding soil, water, and air; they contain chlorophyll, which by photosynthesis can turn sunlight into carbohydrates. Animals, on the contrary, tend to be mobile and more irritable; they obtain complex food from plants and other animals rather than directly from inorganic sources through the aid of chlorophyll.

Inasmuch as plants are necessary for the existence of animals, life is believed to have originated as simple forms of vegetation and to have developed first in the sea.

ORGANIC EVOLUTION

The progressive changes of plants and animals associated with changing physical surroundings throughout geologic time constitute the basis of *organic evolution*. The forms, structures, and functions of organisms have slowly altered during the long ages that have elapsed since the first living things appeared on our globe. Usually evolution has resulted in more highly specialized forms of life and those better adapted to their environment. Simple structures persist longer than complex ones, and structures once lost by a species are never regained. In general, evolution proceeds according to the possibilities and limitations inherent in the organism and the opportunities and restrictions offered by the environment.

Factors of Evolution. To the geologist, evolution is a fact, not a theory, but not all of the causes of evolution are known.

Inheritance of Acquired Characteristics. A theory of organic evolution was proposed in 1801 (in *Système des animaux sans vertèbres*) by Jean Baptiste Lamarck, the founder of invertebrate paleontology. Lamarck thought that the characteristics acquired by an individual in its efforts to satisfy its needs were inherited by its offspring (for example, a giraffe would stretch its neck slightly during a lifetime of reaching for the leaves of trees, and so its offspring would be born with slightly longer necks). This theory of the *inheritance of acquired characteristics* is accepted today by almost no biologists outside of the Soviet Union and other communist states, where it was—for a time, at least—the official doctrine. Lamarck's theory, though not widely accepted during his lifetime, was an influence upon Darwin.

NATURAL SELECTION. The theory of evolution was first presented with convincing evidence in 1859 by Charles Darwin, in his *Origin of Species.* The concept of *natural selection,* based on the *struggle for existence* and the *survival of the fittest,* as the cause of evolution is what is known as *Darwinism;* that is, evolution is a fact, but Darwinism is a theory as to the cause of evolution. Darwin pointed out the following facts. No two plants or animals of the same species are exactly alike (*variation*). Plants and animals produce many more offspring than the environment can support. In a given environment, those individuals better adapted to the environment survive and pass on their characteristics to their descendants, while those not so well adapted perish. Over a long period of time, and with gradual or radical changes in the environment, natural selection may pick those individuals of a species better adapted to the new conditions, resulting in the origin of new species.

An additional factor operative among animals is *sexual selection:* the fact that individuals having certain characteristics that give them an advantage in winning a mate pass on those characteristics to their descendants, while less favored individuals do not win mates and so have no offspring.

MUTATIONS. Present-day evolutionary theory places a great deal of emphasis on *mutations,* which are sudden changes in the *genes,* the agents of heredity. (The genes, contained in the *chromosomes,* are minute bodies that can be "seen" only by means of the electron microscope.) Mutations have been created in the laboratory by a number of methods; in nature, it is now believed, they are caused chiefly by cosmic rays. Some mutations are advantageous to the individual; others are harmful, or even lethal. There is, of course, a tendency for the advantageous mutations to be transmitted and for the individuals possessing them to multiply. The theory of evolution by mutations does not contradict Darwin's theory of natural selection; it merely modifies it. The Dutch scientist Hugo de Vries in 1901 first placed this aspect of biology on a firm basis.

Evidences of Evolution. The doctrine of evolution is supported by several lines of evidence, which are summarized below.

OBSERVATION. Evolutionary changes have been observed in certain species after even short intervals of time.

EXAMPLES: Land snails collected 14 years apart from the same area showed structural alterations. Certain bacteria once vulnerable to antibiotics became, a few years later, immune to them; the present resistant bacteria are the descendants of a few originally immune ancestors.

EXPERIMENTATION. Students of genetics have produced variations in a species (for example, the fruit fly) through controlled experiments. Animal and plant breeders have created a large number of new and specialized forms of life that have never been known before.

EXAMPLES: Maize, or corn, does not exist except in cultivation. All breeds of dogs, from Saint Bernard to Chihuahua, are the descendants of wolflike ancestors.

DISTRIBUTION. The plants and animals of certain isolated places such as islands show both resemblances to and differences from similar species of nearby islands and the nearest mainland. The resemblances indicate a common ancestry, while the differences indicate evolutionary development during the period of isolation.

Furthermore, plants and animals inhabiting similar environments which are separated by a natural barrier are often quite different.

EXAMPLE: The fishes on either side of the Isthmus of Panama do not resemble those on the other side of the Isthmus as much as they do species farther north and south on the same side of the land barrier.

EMBRYOLOGY. During the prenatal development of the organism, which begins as a single cell, nearly all animals pass through stages that correspond successively to the development of the entire race. This is called the *biogenetic law,* or the *law of recapitulation:* "Ontogeny recapitulates phylogeny"; that is, the development of the individual (ontogeny) repeats the history of the race (phylogeny).

EXAMPLE: The embryos of all reptiles, amphibians, birds, and mammals have nonfunctional gills and associated blood vessels, indicating that these classes of animals evolved from fishes.

COMPARATIVE PHYSIOLOGY. The more closely related organisms are, the greater their physiological and biochemical similarities. Such similarities in animals that are not closely related suggest a common, but remote, ancestry.

EXAMPLES: Laboratory tests show that the blood serum of the anthropoid apes is more like that of man than is the blood serum of any other animals. The cow is not closely related to man, but thyroid extract from cattle may be used to increase metabolism in man.

COMPARATIVE ANATOMY. Comparable structures (as well as functions) are found in plants and animals that outwardly bear little resemblance to one another. If the structures are fundamentally the same, even though they may not serve the same function, they are said to be *homologous* and are considered to have the same origin. Structures that are in some ways similar and serve the same function but have fundamental differences and cannot have had the same origin are described as *analogous*. Inherited organs that no longer serve a useful purpose are known as *vestigial structures*.

EXAMPLES: The human arm, the foreleg of a dog, the flipper of a seal, and the wing of a bird have the same kind of skeletal structure and are homologous. The wing of an insect and the wing of a bird, which serve the same function but do not have the same structure and origin, are analogous. The appendix in man is a vestigial structure, of no present value though a necessary part of the digestive system of lower animals.

PALEONTOLOGY. Perhaps the most convincing evidence for evolution is offered by the fossil record, which reveals a constant progression of changing forms of life, from primitive to modern, in rocks of decreasing age.

EXAMPLES: (1) The modern horse has one toe, but fossils of his predecessors have a larger number of digits; the oldest horselike animal, about 1 foot high (Eohippus), had five toes—four functional and one rudimental—on the foreleg. (2) Early nautiloid cephalopods (mollusks) had slightly curved shells, from which developed many types found in younger rocks, including closely coiled shells. Likewise, the sutures of the earliest cephalopods were simple, whereas those of the much later cephalopods known as ammonites became highly intricate in pattern.

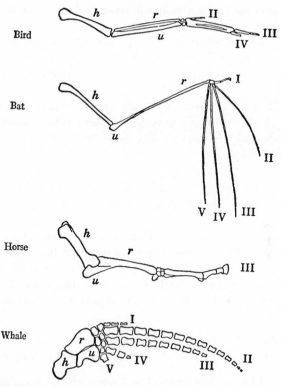

Fig. 36.—Homologous structures in front limb of four animals of unlike kinds and habits. Abbreviations: h, humerus; r, radius; u, ulna. Numbers refer to related bones. (*Modified from various authors.*) (By permission from *Biology*, by Gordon Alexander, copyright, 1954, by Barnes & Noble, Inc.)

FOSSILS

Fossils are the remains and impressions of ancient life, both plant and animal. They range in size from microscopic structures to dinosaur skeletons and complete bodies of woolly mammoths. Skeletons of extinct races of man are considered fossils.

Necessary Conditions. An environment favorable to the growth and later preservation of organisms is required for the occurrence of fossils. Two conditions are almost always present:

1. The possession of *hard parts,* either internal or external, such as bones, teeth, scales, shells, and wood; these parts remain after the rest of the organism has decayed. Organisms that lack

hard parts, such as worms and jellyfish, have left a meager geologic record.

2. *Quick burial* of the dead organism, so that protection is afforded against weathering, bacterial action, and scavengers. Traces and impressions of organisms also need burial to preserve them.

Environments Favoring Preservation. Nature provides many situations in which the remains of animals and plants are protected against destruction. The most likely places for burial are discussed below.

MARINE SEDIMENT. This is by far the most important environment for the preservation of fossils, owing to the incredible richness of marine life. Shells are common in the clear water where limestone forms.

FRESH-WATER SEDIMENT. The beds of former lakes are often prolific sources of fossils. The rapidly accumulating sediments in the channels, floodplains, and deltas of streams bury fresh-water organisms, along with land plants and animals that fall into the water. Quicksand in stream channels is a treacherous trap for animals.

EXAMPLE: The beautifully preserved fossil fish from the Green River oil shale of southwestern Wyoming lived in a vast shallow lake.

BOGS. The swampy ground of former glacial lakes and ponds, overgrown with vegetation, mires many animals, especially large ones.

EXAMPLE: Big Bone Lick, in Kentucky, has yielded more than 100 mastodons; Thomas Jefferson kept skeletons from this bog in his collection in the White House.

TUNDRA. The frigid ground of the north country acts as a remarkable preservative for animal fossils.

EXAMPLE: The woolly mammoth, a long-haired rhinoceros, and other mammals have been periodically exposed in the tundra of Siberia, the hair and red flesh still frozen in cold storage.

ASPHALT. The evaporation of petroleum from oil seeps leaves a sticky residue which slowly hardens into shiny asphalt, attracting animals to their death.

EXAMPLE: The park in Los Angeles called Rancho La Brea is famous for its hundreds of thousands of bones of prehistoric saber-toothed tigers, ground sloths, bears, camels, elephants, and other animals.

VOLCANIC ASH. Extensive falls of volcanic ash and coarser particles overwhelm and bury all forms of life, from flying insects to great trees.

EXAMPLE: The splendid fossil forests of Yellowstone National Park, represented by standing trunks, originated in this manner.

LAVA. Flowing lava may surround living timber, yet the moist wood may not be destroyed by fire, either because it is sealed by the lava from contact with oxygen or because the lava solidifies as a mold around the tree before the wood is consumed.

EXAMPLE: Lava sheets at Craters of the Moon National Monument, Idaho, have preserved the forms of trees while consuming the wood fiber.

WIND-BLOWN SEDIMENT. Dunes seldom yield fossils, but the wind-laid sediments known as loess sometimes do.

EXAMPLES: (1) Dinosaur eggs preserved by drifting sand have been found in Mongolia. (2) Numerous fossil bones of horses have been exposed in loess deposits in Nebraska.

CAVE DEPOSITS. Sought for shelter, caves have preserved the bones of many animals that died in them and were subsequently buried under a blanket of clay or a cover of dripstone. Predatory animals and early man alike brought food to caves to be eaten, leaving bones that paleontologists have discovered.

EXAMPLE: Skeletons of Neanderthal man, the best-known race of extinct man, have been found in caves and rock shelters from Belgium to Palestine.

Modes of Fossilization. Fossils are produced in a number of ways. Natural mummification may take place in the dry air of a cave or desert, and the remains may be buried later by sediment. Bodies may be sealed in a protective medium, such as oil, ice, or resin from trees. Organic material may be replaced by inorganic material, so that the form of the organism will be preserved. The principal types of fossilization are described below.

ORIGINAL PRESERVATION. The more durable parts of some organisms as old as 70 million years or more have been preserved in their original composition and appearance. Younger but no less noteworthy are the complete bodies of Ice Age mammals recovered from the frozen ground of the Arctic.

EXAMPLE: Mollusk shells older than the Rocky Mountains are found in Western shale with the original mother-of-pearl intact.

PETRIFACTION. Also called petrification, this process involves conversion to stone. It is accomplished in the following ways:

1. *Permineralization* is the filling of pores by mineral matter dissolved in ground water.

2. *Replacement* is the substitution of the mineral matter from ground water for the original organic substance. Silica is an especially common replacing compound, resulting in *silicification;* calcium carbonate produces *calcification;* and iron sulfide produces *pyritization.* Every detail of the internal structure may be delicately recorded; or only the outer shape may be preserved, making a false replica, or *pseudomorph.*

3. *Carbonation,* or *distillation,* requires the loss of the volatile elements of an organism and the concentration of the carbon in a residue which outlines the form of the original.

EXAMPLES: (1) Fossil bones, such as those of the huge dinosaurs, are usually petrified, becoming solid and heavy. (2) The outstanding instance of replacement is petrified wood, some of which is of gem quality: agatized, jasperized, opalized. (3) Carbonized fern leaves in shale, frequent in coal mines, are among the most attractive of fossils.

MOLD. When an organic structure embedded in rock later disappears, perhaps dissolved by ground water, there remains an empty space having the exact shape of the object, called a *natural mold.* A thin mold, such as that of a leaf, is called an *imprint.*

EXAMPLE: The most extraordinary natural molds are those of insects in Baltic amber, the hardened resin of trees which grew there 30 to 40 million years ago; the organic tissue has virtually dried away, but the filaments on the antenna of a gnat can be counted.

CAST. If a natural mold is later filled with mineral matter, a *natural cast* is produced.

EXAMPLE: Soluble marine shells often leave, in the hardened mud, natural molds which are afterward filled with quartz.

IMPRESSION. Footprints, trails, and burrows are the *impressions* of animals which have moved through the sediment or along the ground before lithification took place.

EXAMPLES: Worm burrows in rocks in Montana and Canada are the oldest animal fossils. Excellently preserved footprints in the shaly sandstone of the Connecticut River Valley record the passage of dinosaurs across an ancient floodplain.

COPROLITE. Fossilized excrement of animals, known as *coprolite*, reveals by its contents the feeding habits of ancient animals.

CLASSIFICATION OF FOSSILS

Taxonomy is the science of classifying plants and animals according to their natural relationships. Organisms are classified first of all as belonging to either the plant or animal kingdom; intermediate forms of life are classed as the Protista. The successively smaller categories of classification are as follows: *kingdom—phylum* (plural, *phyla*)—*class—order—family—genus* (plural, *genera*)—*species—race, breed,* or *variety.* Subordinate groupings, such as *subphyla,* are also used where desirable.

As the basic working unit of classification, the species is defined as a group of like individuals who interbreed among themselves, but cannot interbreed with members of any other group.

The binomial (two-name) system of nomenclature provides each organism with a double Latin name—the name of the genus (capitalized), followed by the name of the species (uncapitalized) —both printed in italics, as *Homo sapiens,* the scientific name of modern man.

Classifications are not universally agreed upon. The most widely adopted system of plant classification, based largely on anatomical and morphological criteria, is that of Tippo. The following table lists in a condensed outline the more recent divisions of the plant and animal kingdoms.*

* Reprinted from *Biology* by Gordon Alexander, Copyright, 1954, by Barnes & Noble, Inc.

An interesting and thorough survey of paleontology is *Fossils: An Introduction to Prehistoric Life* by William H. Matthews III, 1962, Barnes & Noble, Inc.

PLANT KINGDOM

Subkingdom. Thallophyta. Plants not forming embryos.

Phylum 1. Cyanophyta. Blue-green algae.
Phylum 2. Euglenophyta. Flagellates.
Phylum 3. Chlorophyta. Green algae.
Phylum 4. Chrysophyta. Yellow-green algae, golden brown algae, diatoms.
Phylum 5. Pyrrophyta. Cryptomonads, dinoflagellates.
Phylum 6. Phaeophyta. Brown algae.
Phylum 7. Rhodophyta. Red algae.
Phylum 8. Schizomycophyta. Bacteria.
Phylum 9. Myxomycophyta. Slime molds.
Phylum 10. Eumycophyta. True fungi.

Subkingdom. Embryophyta. Plants forming embryos.

Phylum 11. Bryophyta or Atracheata. Plants lacking vascular tissues.
   Class 1. Musci. Mosses.
   Class 2. Hepaticae. Liverworts.
   Class 3. Anthocerotae. Hornworts.
Phylum 12. Tracheophyta or Tracheata. Plants with vascular tissues.
   Subphylum 1. Psilopsida. Psilopsids.
   Subphylum 2. Lycopsida. Club mosses.
   Subphylum 3. Sphenopsida. Horsetails and relatives.
   Subphylum 4. Pteropsida. Ferns and seed plants.
   Class 1. Filicineae. Ferns.
   Class 2. Gymnospermae. Cone-bearing plants and relatives.
     Subclass 1. Cycadophytae
     Subclass 2. Coniferophytae
   Class 3. Angiospermae. True flowering plants.
     Subclass 1. Dicotyledoneae.
     Subclass 2. Monocotyledoneae.

ANIMAL KINGDOM

Phylum 1. Protozoa. Unicellular animals.
   Class 1. Mastigophora. Flagellate protozoa (e.g., *Euglena*).
   Class 2. Sarcodina. Amoeboid protozoa (e.g., *Amoeba*).
   Class 3. Sporozoa. Spore-producing protozoa (e.g., *Plasmodium*).
   Class 4. Infusoria. Ciliate protozoa (e.g., *Paramecium*).
Phylum 2. Porifera. Sponges.
Phylum 3. Coelenterata.
   Class 1. Hydrozoa. Hydroids (e.g., *Hydra, Obelia*).
   Class 2. Scyphozoa. Jellyfishes.
   Class 3. Anthozoa. Corals and sea anemones.
Phylum 4. Ctenophora. Comb jellies or sea walnuts.
Phylum 5. Platyhelminthes. Flatworms.

Class 1. Turbellaria. *Planaria* and related animals.
Class 2. Trematoda. Flukes.
Class 3. Cestoda. Tapeworms.
Phylum 6. Nemertea. Nemertine worms.
Phylum 7. Nematoda. Roundworms.
Phylum 8. Rotatoria. Rotifers.
Phylum 9 Nematomorpha. Horsehair worms.
Phylum 10. Bryozoa. Moss animals.
Phylum 11. Brachiopoda. Lamp shells.
Phylum 12. Echinodermata.
Class 1. Asteroidea. Starfishes.
Class 2. Ophiuroidea. Brittle stars, serpent stars.
Class 3. Echinoidea. Sea urchins, sand dollars.
Class 4. Holothuroidea. Sea cucumbers, sea slugs.
Class 5. Crinoidea. Crinoids (sea lilies).
Phylum 13. Mollusca. Mollusks.
Class 1. Pelecypoda. Clams, mussels, oysters.
Class 2. Amphineura. Chitons.
Class 3. Gastropoda. Snails, slugs.
Class 4. Scaphopoda. Tooth shells.
Class 5. Cephalopoda. Squids, octopus, nautilus.
Phylum 14. Annelida. Segmented worms.
Class 1. Chaetopoda. Earthworms, clamworms.
Class 2. Hirudinea. Leeches.
Phylum 15. Onychophora. *Peripatus.*
Phylum 16. Arthropoda.
Class 1. Crustacea. Crayfish, crabs, barnacles, water fleas.
Class 2. Diplopoda. Millipedes.
Class 3. Chilopoda. Centipedes.
Class 4. Insecta. Insects: bees, grasshoppers, beetles, flies, etc.
Class 5. Arachnida. Ticks, spiders, scorpions, horseshoe crab.
Phylum 17. Chordata.
Subphylum 1. Hemichorda. *Dolichoglossus.*
Subphylum 2. Urochorda. Tunicates: sea squirts, sea pork.
Subphylum 3. Cephalochorda. *Amphioxus.*
Subphylum 4. Vertebrata. Vertebrates.
Class 1. Agnatha. Lampreys, hagfishes.
Class 2. Chondrichthyes. Sharks, rays.
Class 3. Osteichthyes. Bony fishes: perch, trout, catfish, eel.
Class 4. Amphibia. Salamanders, frogs, toads.
Class 5. Reptilia. Turtles, snakes, lizards, alligators.
Class 6. Aves. Birds: ostrich, chicken, sparrow, robin.
Class 7. Mammalia. Mammals: opossum, squirrel, rat, bat, whale, horse, man.

REVIEW QUESTIONS

1. How might the earth's early atmosphere have differed from the the present one?
2. How do plants differ from animals?
3. List six lines of evidence for evolution, and give an example of each.
4. What is the biogenetic law and how does it operate?
5. What are analogous, vestigial, and homologous structures?
6. Name the two conditions necessary for the presence of fossils.
7. Describe eight environments favorable for the preservation of fossils.
8. What is the difference between permineralization, replacement, and carbonation?
9. How does a cast replace a mold?
10. What does the scientific name for man, *Homo sapiens,* mean in terms of classification?

20

Interpretation of Geologic History

Geology has been spoken of as "the historical science" because it deals with the order of happenings within a specific framework of place and time. The sequence of events that have taken place on the earth in any given area during any given interval of geologic time is determined by many varied geologic techniques and procedures. There are a number of fundamental methods based upon the principles of physical geology (discussed in Part I of this book) and the rules of historical geology.

THE GEOLOGIC RECORD

The study of *stratified* (layered) rocks is called *stratigraphy,* and the stratigraphic unit is a *formation*. Each formation consists of an aggregation of related *strata* (rock layers), separated from each other by surfaces of easy separation called *bedding planes*. These units of strata must be characteristic enough to be distinguished from the beds immediately above and below them and sufficiently thick and extensive to appear on a geologic map. Although some of the earlier recognized formations were given descriptive names, the present custom is to name them after the place (any geographic name) where they were originally described —the *type locality* (as the "Green River formation"). If the kind of rock is fairly uniform, the name may appear, for example, as "Green River shale." A complex formation may be further broken down into its somewhat different constituent layers, which are referred to as *members* and given individual names, such as the "Cannonball member" of the "Fort Union formation." This member, in turn, consists of individual unnamed *beds* (or *laminae,* if less than 1 centimeter thick). Two or more adjoining formations having certain prominent features in common may be considered together as a *group* (as the "Newark group"). For mapping purposes, units of igneous and metamorphic rocks, though not stratified, are identified as formations, such as "Pikes Peak granite."

The succession of rock formations in a given place, such as the face of a canyon wall, a mine shaft, or a well hole, when shown in a vertical chart, is called a *columnar section*. A composite record, bringing together the columnar sections from a number of localities, constitutes a *geologic column*. When the rocks are dated by intervals of geologic time, a complete record of the geologic history of the region may be presented in diagrammatic form.

U. S. Geological Survey   *Kirschner*

Fig. 37—Ripple marks. Oil Bay, Alaska.

Superposition. When books are put in a pile, one by one, the first laid down is on the bottom and the last is on the top. Sedimentary rocks and lava flows accumulate in the same way, so that if the layers are undisturbed their relative ages are known. This simple but basic principle is the *law of superposition*.

Rocks that have been tilted or even overturned by folding or displaced by faulting do not present such a simple sequence, and it is a problem for the geologist to determine the original arrangement. He knows of numerous ways to tell the top from the bottom stratum. For instance, *mud cracks* in drying sediment narrow downward; *ripple marks, rill marks, wave marks,* and *raindrop impressions* lie upon the original surface of a layer; and gas escaping from cooling lava leaves oval cavities toward the top.

Faunal Succession. One of the basic laws of historical geology is that each sedimentary formation contains its own assemblage of fossils, characteristic of the place and time in which the organisms lived. This is the *law of faunal succession,* which derives from the fact that the animals and plants when alive occupied a particular *habitat* (environment) suitable to them, and had reached a particular stage in their evolution. Older rocks yield fossils of more primitive organisms, and younger rocks yield among others more advanced and complex organisms.

Unconformities. Gaps in the geologic record are known as *unconformities.* Certain layers may have been removed by erosion before later ones were added, or there may have been no deposition at all during an interval of time. If the beds are parallel above and below the unconformity, the structure is called a *disconformity.* If the upper rocks lie upon an eroded surface of a different major type of rock (as sedimentary on igneous or metamorphic), the relationship is called a *nonconformity.* The most conspicuous kind of unconformity is the *angular unconformity,* where two groups of sedimentary rocks with different angles of dip are in depositional contact, indicating that the lower sequence of strata was tilted or folded before being eroded and covered by the upper sequence.

CORRELATION

To reconstruct the geologic history of any area it is necessary to determine the sequence of all the geologic events that happened. Then these events and the resulting formations must be related in time with those of other areas. Establishing these time equivalences is known as *correlation.*

Difficulties of Correlation. If formations were uniformly distributed throughout the world, correlating them would be simple. However, no single area in the world contains the complete record of geologic events. Warping and uplift of the earth's crust have gone on irregularly, with erosion at one place and deposition elsewhere. In addition, internal and external vulcanism have occurred in various regions. Certain great difficulties must, therefore, be faced in geologic work:

1. Formations are limited in extent. The *law of original continuity* states that strata either thin out as a result of decreasing deposition or terminate against the side of the basin in which they were deposited.

2. Formations differ from place to place. This *lateral variation*

may be illustrated by the sequence of sediments which make up
the strata laid down by a stream in its journey from the mountains to the ocean. Conglomerate deposited near the mountains

FIG. 38A—Nonconformity between columnar basalt (above) and sandstone
beds (below). Little Falls, New Jersey.

FIG. 38B—Angular unconformity. Ouray, Colorado.

grades into sandstone, which then becomes shale as the transporting power of the stream is further reduced. Beyond the shoreline, in open water, the formation may grade into limestone.

Rocks of the same age that were formed in different environments of deposition are said to represent different *sedimentary facies*. In different facies the types of animal and plant fossils are different. Fluctuating conditions, such as between land and sea, cause facies to *interfinger*, or *intertongue*.

3. Formations may be displaced by faulting, may be buried deeply by downfolding, or may be altered by metamorphism so that the order of deposition is difficult and sometimes impossible to determine.

4. Only a small proportion of the animals and plants that once lived have left fossil remains or traces.

Means of Correlation. Given the laws of superposition and organic evolution, the correlation of rocks becomes a matter of making comparisons. Some methods of correlation can be used only with surface exposures, while others are applicable to underground work with drill cores and broken cuttings from wells, or with geophysical data obtained indirectly and based on the differences in behavior of different rock types in relation to the transmission of seismic waves, electrical conductivity, etc.

CONTINUOUS OUTCROPS. Exposed strata may sometimes be traced by observation over a considerable distance of many miles, but usually only in canyon and plateau country.

SIMILAR LITHOLOGY. When a formation changes little from place to place, its rock nature (mineral composition, texture, color, and geophysical data) aids in correlation. The presence of a noteworthy peculiarity, such as odd concretions, may make correlation possible even when the normal characteristics vary. Similarity of weathering effects, metamorphism, structures such as folds and joints, *topographic expression* (whether it forms ridges or valleys), and soil may be helpful.

PERSISTENT THICKNESS. Generally, thickness is quite variable, but some formations are fairly uniform in this respect, and such uniformity aids correlation.

SIMILAR POSITIONS. The relative position of a formation in a sequence is highly valuable information for correlating rocks. The larger the number of formations accessible for comparison, and the stronger the contrast between them, the more certain is this method. A black limestone is not unique, but if it occurs between a green shale and a white sandstone, the likelihood of its being recognized is much increased. Unconformities serve the same function in locating formations. A *key horizon* (specific level or layer) of especial distinctiveness is picked for correlating between widely separated places.

INDEX, OR GUIDE, FOSSILS. The most reliable criterion for correlation over long distances, in complex structures, and beneath the surface (even in well cuttings) is supplied by paleontology. Certain fossils (called "index fossils" or "guide fossils") are extremely useful in the identification of formations, because they are typical of particular strata. Especially suitable as index fossils are those organisms which can float or swim and thus may be distributed over a wide area. Another requisite for a species that will serve as a guide fossil is a relatively short existence in the geologic time scale; a limited *stratigraphic* (vertical) distribution of fossils restricts the time interval of the rocks in which they lie to a range convenient for the purposes of the geologist. Microscopic forms are usually the best preserved and most numerous, but organisms possessing complicated structures are better guides than those that are simple, because their evolutionary changes can be more readily detected. In the absence of index fossils, an association of less distinctive fossils is sometimes helpful for correlation purposes.

RADIOACTIVITY DATING. Correlation by means of radioactivity determinations (as described below, p. 189) is especially useful for ancient rocks devoid of fossils. Within its limits of accuracy it can give ages in actual years.

GEOLOGIC TIME

Although the evolutionary changes in life, as revealed by fossils, leave in the rocks their record of the passage of time, the comparisons are relative only. Nevertheless, the resolving power of biochronology is so great that it is able, for instance, to distinguish no less than 58 world-wide zones of ammonites in rocks of Jurassic age. The basic problem still remains, however, of determining the absolute ages, in years, of rocks in the earth's crust and of accurately gauging the immensity of geologic time.

Rate of Sedimentation. Elaborate attempts have been made to determine the total age of the earth, or the duration of certain eras, by the rate of sedimentation. Time estimates are arrived at by measuring the thickness of layers of rock and multiplying these figures by the rate at which the layers are estimated to have been deposited. However, the process of sedimentation is so erratic that it is not a reliable indicator. The rate of erosion also varies, being more rapid today than at many times in the past.

Salinity of the Ocean. The rate at which salt is being added to the seas as the land is worn away has been used in an effort to calculate the length of geologic time. The varying rate of erosion and the lack of knowledge about several factors involved therein prevent this method from being useful.

Radioactivity. Accurate estimates of geologic time and of the ages of minerals and rocks are being determined by the application of the principles of radioactivity (see p. 23). Certain radioactive elements, particularly uranium, disintegrate at a constant rate that is evidently unaffected by heat, pressure, or other natural conditions, and release new elements, ending with inert lead. By measuring the number of lead atoms present in a specific quantity of uranium it is possible to determine with a high degree of accuracy the length of time the transformation has been taking place. This method is especially applicable to igneous rocks in which the uranium minerals crystallized from a magma or primary solution and immediately began their systematic disintegration without undue loss of the products of transformation.

A given quantity of uranium will yield $\dfrac{1}{7,600,000,000}$ of that amount of lead in one year. The ratio of lead of radioactive origin to uranium present in an unweathered sample of igneous rock is calculated; when multiplied by the fraction shown (with appropriate corrections), the age of the rock can be found. Thus, 1 gram of lead to 76 grams of uranium would mean $\dfrac{1}{76} \times 7,600,000,000$, or about 100,000,000 years.

Other ratios of radioactive elements besides lead-uranium have been used to determine the age of rocks. The helium-uranium ratio, which once seemed so promising, has fallen into disfavor. The ratio between several different *isotopes* (kinds, differing in atomic weight) of lead seems to be reliable. The decay of potassium to argon and of rubidium to strontium yields further ratios of widespread application, which are being actively investigated as a means of learning the age of rocks. For dates more recent than about 40,000 years ago, the radiocarbon method, which measures the amount of the isotope known as Carbon 14 in matter of organic origin, is revealing fascinating information about both geology and archeology.

Law of Intrusion. The age of sedimentary rocks can be determined on the basis of their spatial relationship to associated igneous rocks. The *law of intrusion* states that an igneous body that cuts across another rock is the younger of the two. (For extrusive rocks, the igneous body that rests upon another rock is the younger.) Rocks that are metamorphosed must have been in position before any igneous intrusion that may have caused the metamorphism.

Geologic Time Scale. The construction of the geologic time scale or chart is one of the most significant achievements of geologists. This gargantuan calendar of the past is as fundamental to historical geology, and as indispensable, as the alphabet is to reading or the multiplication table to arithmetic. It is given in Table 5, p. 191.

The oldest time intervals are shown, as is customary, at the bottom, in the order in which the rocks of those ages normally occur in the earth. *The time chart must be memorized,* and it should be learned from the bottom up.

Subdivisions of Geologic Time. The largest segments of geologic time are called *eras.* These are separated from one another by major orogenic (mountain-making) events known as *revolutions,* which were probably world-wide in scope and profoundly affected life on the earth. The eras are named according to the characteristic type of life that flourished, and the names are terms that end in *-zoic* (from Greek *zoe,* life): *Archeozoic* (era of ancient life), *Proterozoic* (era of former life), *Paleozoic* (era of old life), *Mesozoic* (era of middle life), and *Cenozoic* (era of recent life). The rock units of an era are spoken of as a *group.*

Eras are divided into *periods,* which are separated from one another by less extensive local orogenies called *disturbances;* in some places these have been accompanied by uplift of the land and consequent withdrawal of the sea from the low parts of the continents most subject to repeated inundations. Many of the

TABLE 5
GEOLOGIC TIME CHART

Era	Period	Epoch	Duration in Millions of Years	Began Millions of Years Ago	Animals	Plants
Cenozoic	Quaternary	Recent	(Late archeologic and historic time) 1	1	Mammals	Modern seed plants
		Pleistocene				
	Tertiary	Pliocene	12	13		
		Miocene	12	25		
		Oligocene	11	36		
		Eocene	22	58		
		Paleocene	5	63		
Mesozoic	Cretaceous	(Early, Middle, or Late)	72	135	Reptiles and ammonites	Ancient seed plants
	Jurassic		46	181		
	Triassic		49	230		
Paleozoic	Permian	(Early, Middle, or Late)	50	280	Amphibians	Spore-bearing plants
	Carboniferous: Pennsylvanian and Mississippian		30	310		
	Devonian		35	345	Age of fishes	Seaweeds
	Silurian		60	405		
	Ordovician		20	425	Invertebrates	
	Cambrian		75	500		
			100	600		
Pre-Cambrian: Proterozoic and Archeozoic			900 (undetermined)	1,500	Indirect evidence of life	

period names refer to districts where rocks of that age were first studied, such as *Devonian* from Devonshire in England and *Cretaceous* in reference to the chalk (Latin *creta*) deposits on both sides of the English Channel. Others, such as the names *Ordovician* and *Silurian,* are less obvious. These are derived from the names of two Celtic tribes that during Roman times inhabited the parts of Wales in which these formations were first studied. An exception to this locality nomenclature is the division of the Cenozoic era into the *Tertiary* ("third") and *Quaternary* ("fourth") periods. The rock units that belong to a given period constitute a *system.*

The periods are subdivided into *epochs,* which are often separated by retreats of the sea on a regional scale. The more recent epochs, about which more geologic detail is known, are those of the Cenozoic era, as listed in Table 5. The epochs are designated in two ways: (1) periods of the earlier eras (Paleozoic and Mesozoic) are subdivided into *Early, Middle,* and *Late* (as *Early Devonian*); and (2) the Cenozoic era is divided as follows: the Tertiary period into the following epochs: *Paleocene* (*paleo-*, old), *Eocene* (*eo-*, dawn), *Oligocene* (*oligo-*, a few), *Miocene* (*mio-*, less), and *Pliocene* (*plio-*, more); and the Quaternary period into the *Pleistocene* (*pleisto-*, more) and *Recent* epochs. The rock units of a given epoch are spoken of as a *series,* and may be further designated as *Lower, Middle,* and *Upper*—or geographic names may be used.

Epochs are subdivided into *ages.* The rock units that belong to a given age constitute a *stage,* which may be subdivided into *substages.* Still smaller units, *zones,* are named according to their characteristic assemblage of fossils.

Inasmuch as organic evolution is affected by changes in the environment, divisions of time correspond, at least in a general way, to the transformations in the structure and topography of the earth. Thus geologic time is based ultimately upon the interplay of physical and biologic changes.

PALEOGEOGRAPHY

Because the land is constantly warping and the sea level is fluctuating, the present geography of the surface of our planet is a transient thing, its history brief in terms of geology. The study of ancient lands and seas is *paleogeography*. On paleogeographic maps are reconstructed the patterns of continents and oceans, islands and seaways of the past, as determined from the evidence of the rocks and their fossils.

Paleoclimatology, the study of ancient climates, examines the distribution of soils, sand dunes, salt deposits, coral reefs and other fossils, and glacial deposits.

The roots of vanished mountains, with their folded, faulted, intruded, and metamorphosed structures, bear testimony to the ranges that once existed. Fossils of water-dwelling organisms indicate the former distribution of water and whether it was salt or fresh, deep or shallow. Fossils of land organisms tell much about the former climate, altitude, and topography. The agents of erosion, transportation, and deposition are identified by the nature of the sediment and the forms it has assumed. The source of sediment is indicated by the direction in which it becomes coarser and thicker. In these ways the story of the history of the earth is patiently pieced together by thousands of geologists. The main outlines of their findings are presented in the next four chapters of this book, one chapter for each of the great divisions of geologic time.

REVIEW QUESTIONS

1. What is a formation?
2. How are rock strata generally named?
3. What is a columnar section?
4. What is the significance of the law of superposition?
5. Explain the law of faunal succession.
6. Describe three kinds of unconformities.
7. What is the law of original continuity?
8. What causes a facies to intertongue?
9. What are the methods of correlation?
10. Explain the significance of a key horizon and an index fossil.
11. How is radioactivity used to find the age of an igneous rock?
12. What is the law of intrusion?
13. On what basis are eras separated from one another?
14. How are periods divided?
15. What is an epoch? A series?
16. What does a paleogeographic map show?

21

Pre-Cambrian Eras

The interval of enormous length (perhaps 4 to 4.5 billion years *) that stretches from the beginning of geologic time (when the first rocks were formed) to the start of the Cambrian period in the Paleozoic era, is known as Pre-Cambrian time. It is usually divided into two eras, the *Archeozoic* and the *Proterozoic* (see p. 190), each of which is further divided into two periods, named after regions, as indicated below. The Archeozoic era is of unknown length; the Proterozoic era began at least 2 billion years ago. There is a growing tendency to abandon the terms Archeozoic and Proterozoic in favor of a triple subdivision of the Pre-Cambrian using the terms Lower (Keewatin), Middle (Timiskaming) and Upper (Huronian and Keeweenawan), based upon three episodes of regional diastrophism and granitic intrusion in Canada. Radioactive dating of rocks shows a concentration around 2500, 1700, and 950 million years ago.

1. Archeozoic era:
    a. *Keewatin period* (Keewatin is an Indian name for the region north and west of the Great Lakes, where rocks of this period are exposed).

    b. *Timiskaming period* (named for Lake Timiskaming between Ontario and Quebec). The Algoman orogeny and its accompanying granite intrusions mark the end of the Archeozoic era.

* Only a few years ago the age of the earth was generally considered, by astronomers and geologists, to be about 2 billion years. Estimates of cosmic time and space are periodically enlarged. The figure of 4–5 billion years is actually based on an extrapolation of uranium-lead age data, as no rocks composing the original "crust" of the earth have ever been found. The oldest rocks so far dated are of the order of 3.3 billion years. Such an age is supported by age determinations on meteorites which are in agreement at about 4.5 billion years. This suggests that the earth and the solar system originated at the same time, close to 5 billion years ago.

2. Proterozoic era:

    a. Huronian period (named for Lake Huron; Huronian rocks are found north of Lake Huron and around Lake Superior).

    b. Keweenawan period (named for Keweenaw Point on the south shore of Lake Superior; Keweenawan rocks are found around the south and west shores of Lake Superior and other parts of the Canadian Shield). The Killarney orogeny and its accompanying granite intrusions mark the end of the Proterozoic era and of Pre-Cambrian time.

Pre-Cambrian rocks are presumed to be world-wide in extent, but throughout four-fifths of the continental areas they are buried under younger rocks. They are exposed in two main types of occurrences:

1. The stable, so-called shield areas of the earth, which have neither been thickly covered nor profoundly eroded since the end of the Pre-Cambrian.

2. (a) The cores of folded mountain ranges, where they have been exposed to view by large-scale uplift and deep erosion. (b) A few gorges cut deeply into high plateaus give similar exposures.

PHYSICAL HISTORY

The Pre-Cambrian record is so uncertain that only the most general information can be given about these ancient rocks, which are deformed and metamorphosed and nearly devoid of fossils, and are therefore difficult to decipher and to correlate. A systematic presentation of the paleogeography (see p. 192) of the Pre-Cambrian eras is not possible. But we shall consider a few of the regions in which Pre-Cambrian rocks are exposed.

Canadian Shield. The largest surface area of Pre-Cambrian rocks in the world—covering 1,800,000 square miles, about one-half of Canada—is the *Canadian,* or *Laurentian, Shield.* The ground slopes toward Hudson Bay from all sides and the rocks are probably continuous with similar rocks mostly covered by glaciers in Greenland.

Archeozoic Era. The two periods of the Archeozoic era are the Keewatin and the Timiskaming periods.

Keewatin Period. The *Keewatin system* of rocks belongs to the Keewatin period of the Archeozoic era and includes the oldest known rocks in North America. These rocks consist of sediments and lava flows and were all thoroughly metamorphosed after being deposited. Among the best-known Keewatin rocks are the *Coutchiching series,* the *Soudan formation,* the *Wawa series,* the *Grenville series,* and the *Hastings series.* The Keewatin period was followed by a strong deformation known as the *Laurentian disturbance,* which was accompanied by the intrusion of *Laurentian granite* (now chiefly altered to gneiss), and followed by a long interval of erosion which left a pronounced unconformity.

Timiskaming Period. The next period, the Timiskaming, was marked by a substantial deposition of sedimentary rocks, the *Timiskaming system,* which were later metamorphosed to their present condition. The *Knife Lake* and *Seine River series* belong here. This period was followed by the *Algoman revolution,* of great intensity, and the intrusion of Algoman granite on a gigantic scale, which affected all the earlier rocks.

PROTEROZOIC ERA. The two periods of the Proterozoic era are the Huronian and the Keweenawan periods.

Huronian Period. After another unconformity, more complete than the previous one, the Proterozoic era saw the deposition of rocks of the Huronian period. In a downwarped trough called the *Ontarian geosyncline* the sea came in, surrounded by high land masses. Within this seaway, and on land as well, were deposited sediments, though not continuously; they are divided into the *Bruce series, Cobalt series* (including the *Gowganda formation*), and *Animikie series* (including the *Lorrain formation*), all metamorphosed at a later time. Erosion produced an unconformity at the close of the Huronian period.

Keweenawan Period. The Keweenawan period is noteworthy for renewed igneous activity of both intrusive and extrusive types. The Keweenawan period came to a close with the enormous intrusions of *Killarney granite* during the *Killarney,* or *Penokean, revolution.* Mountains were formed in three widely separated places in southeastern Canada, and were eroded over a long period, producing the most extensive unconformity known in this part of the world.

Fig. 39—Grand Canyon of the Colorado River, showing erosion surfaces and Inner Gorge.

Grand Canyon. Small but very instructive exposures of Pre-Cambrian rocks occur in the Inner Gorge of the Grand Canyon, in Arizona.

ARCHEOZOIC ERA. The Archeozoic rocks exposed in the "Granite Gorge" belong to the *Vishnu series,* which is actually mainly schist of sedimentary origin. The schist was folded into mountains, intruded by large granite masses and many pegmatite dikes, and recrystallized during the *Mazatzal revolution.*

PROTEROZOIC ERA. An unconformity representing prolonged peneplanation separates the Vishnu schist from the *Unkar* and *Chuar series,* which comprise the *Grand Canyon system* of the Proterozoic era. Once lying as horizontal sedimentary beds and lava flows, probably deposited in a vast sedimentary trough, the series now occurs in faulted blocks formed during the *Grand Canyon disturbance.* They are only slightly metamorphosed. After the Grand Canyon orogeny, extensive erosion produced another unconformity, which marks the upper limit of the Pre-Cambrian in this region.

Northern Rocky Mountains. Perhaps continuous with the geosyncline in which the Proterozoic rocks of the Grand Canyon were deposited was another sinking trough which extended from Arizona and Colorado into western Canada. In this basin or group of basins accumulated a thick layer of sediment derived from the west and now representing the largest known area of Proterozoic rocks. These rocks are called the *Beltian system* and are best observed in the Little Belt Mountains of Montana. The rocks have been altered little since they were laid down, although they have been subjected to considerable uplift and gentle warping, followed by peneplanation.

Other Continents. Pre-Cambrian rocks, similar to those already described, are exposed in extensive outcroppings in South America (especially the Guiana and Amazonian Shields), Europe (chiefly the Baltic Shield of Scandinavia and Finland), India (Indian Shield), Siberia (Angara Shield), Africa (south of the Sahara Desert), and Australia (Australian Shield).

MINERAL RESOURCES

Immensely valuable mineral deposits of Pre-Cambrian age are found on all the continents. The great amount of igneous activity and the long period of time involved were favorable to the formation of many metallic and nonmetallic mineral bodies, which are now accessible because of subsequent uplift and erosion.

Gold. Billions of dollars' worth of gold have come from the Porcupine, Kirkland Lake, and other mining districts in the shield area of eastern Canada. By far the world's richest gold producer is the Rand (Witwatersrand), in Pre-Cambrian rocks of the Union of South Africa, with a total yield approaching 10 billion dollars. Deep gold mines in Brazil and the Kolar district of India and the extraordinary deposits of Kalgoorlie in western Australia, are of Pre-Cambrian origin, as is gold in Siberia.

Silver. The Pre-Cambrian silver deposits at Cobalt, Ontario, and elsewhere in the Canadian Shield are among the most important ever discovered. They are often associated with nickel and cobalt.

Uranium. The two most important deposits of pitchblende and other uranium-bearing minerals have been found in the Pre-Cambrian rocks of the Belgian Congo and northern Canada (especially near Great Bear Lake).

Nickel. Nearly all of the world's nickel comes from the Pre-Cambrian rocks at Sudbury, Ontario. With the nickel are gold, silver, platinum, palladium, copper, iron, and other minerals.

Copper. The important and unique deposits of native copper of the Keweenaw Peninsula in northern Michigan are Pre-Cambrian in age. Their economic importance has declined, due to depletion, but nothing similar has been found elsewhere. Copper of this age is important in the Baltic region and Siberia.

Iron. In various parts of the globe during the Proterozoic era, sedimentary iron ores were deposited on a prodigious scale unequaled in later geologic time. The Mesabi and other sedimentary "iron ranges" in the Soudan formation of the Lake Superior region, recently discovered deposits in Quebec and Labrador, and huge deposits in Brazil and Venezuela are supplying man with his most essential metal. Pre-Cambrian iron is important in China.

CLIMATE

There is no evidence that the climates of Pre-Cambrian time were very different, on the whole, from those of later eras. Our only source of information regarding climate is the record in the rocks. Fossil evidence is scanty. The rocks seem to be of normal types.

The most significant aspect of Pre-Cambrian climate is the evidence of extensive glaciation in North America, Australia, South Africa, and China, as well as of glaciation (that is very ancient but not accurately dated) in India, Greenland, and Norway. The glacial material in the Gowganda formation of the Huronian period is of exceptional interest; it has been identified over a distance of 1,000 miles in central Canada.

PLANTS AND ANIMALS

The most profound difference between the Pre-Cambrian world and the earth as it appears today lies in the primitive nature of marine life and the almost total lack of evidence of land life. The apparent sudden emergence of a host of plants and animals at the beginning of the Cambrian period, however, strongly suggests that organisms must have been developing for a long while during the earlier eras. The oldest known structures are those from the Gunflint formation of Ontario, dating between 1.7 and 2.1 billion years ago.

The quantity of graphitic carbon in some Pre-Cambrian rocks points to an abundance of life in the sea. Pre-Cambrian organisms are assumed to have lacked the shells and other hard structures conducive to preservation as fossils. Thick beds of Pre-Cambrian limestone and stratified iron deposits are most readily explained as resulting from the action of living organisms.

Deposits of calcareous algae constitute the principal fossils of Pre-Cambrian age. These are microscopic plants which grow in colonies and precipitate calcium carbonate in concentric layers. They are found in the Canadian Shield, the Grand Canyon, and the Beltian region of Montana.

Worm trails and burrows in the Beltian rocks are the best indications of Pre-Cambrian animal life. The discovery in 1965 of small fossil brachiopods 720 million years old in the Canadian Arctic has expanded our vistas of Pre-Cambrian evolution.

REVIEW QUESTIONS

1. Name in order the subdivisions of the Archeozoic era.
2. Name in order the subdivisions of the Proterozoic era.
3. In what two types of occurrence are Pre-Cambrian rocks exposed?

4. Where is the largest exposure of Pre-Cambrian rocks in North America?
5. Identify the following: Laurentian disturbance, Algoman revolution, Killarney revolution, Mazatzal revolution, Grand Canyon disturbance.
6. What and where is the Beltian system of rocks?
7. Name the main mineral resources of Pre-Cambrian age.
8. Describe the oldest known glacial interval.
9. What are the most common Pre-Cambrian plant fossils?
10. What Pre-Cambrian animal remains have been found?

22
Paleozoic Era

With the opening of the Paleozoic era geologic history assumes a character that can be interpreted with some confidence. In general, the rocks have been less buried, metamorphosed, and eroded, the fossils are more numerous, and correlation is more definite—in extreme instances the difference between the Pre-Cambrian and the Paleozoic is like that between a well-printed book in our own language and a fragmentary manuscript written in a strange tongue.

PALEOZOIC PERIODS

The Paleozoic era, beginning possibly 600 million years ago, is divided into seven periods, equal in status though unequal in length. These are, in chronological order, as follows:

1. *Cambrian period,* from Cambria, the Latin name for Wales. Type locality, Wales; standard section, Wales and western England. Duration 100 million years.

2. *Ordovician period,* from Ordovices, a Celtic people inhabiting part of Wales in Roman times. Type locality and standard section, Wales. Duration, 75 million years.

3. *Silurian period,* from Silures, a people of ancient Britain. Type locality and standard section, Wales and western England. Duration, 20 million years.

4. *Devonian period,* from Devonshire, England. Type locality, Wales and southwestern England; standard section, western Germany. Duration, 60 million years.*

5. *Mississippian period.* Type locality and standard section, central Mississippi Valley. Duration, 35 million years.

6. *Pennsylvanian period.* Type locality, Pennsylvania; standard section, western Pennsylvania and adjoining parts of Ohio and West Virginia. Duration, 30 million years.

* The earliest systematic study of the Paleozoic sedimentary formations was made in Britain, which accounts for the type localities being largely in England and Wales.

The Mississippian and Pennsylvanian periods are sometimes grouped together as the *Carboniferous period,* because of their coal-bearing strata, and are approximately equivalent to the European Lower and Upper Carboniferous periods, respectively.

7. *Permian period,* from Perm, a former province in Russia. Type locality and standard section, northeastern Russia. Duration, 50 million years.

NORTH AMERICAN LANDS AND SEAS

Seven major structural features (listed below) dominated the physical geography of North America during the Paleozoic. Although they did not all originate at the same time, and each did not always maintain the same size, shape, and position throughout this era, the paleogeography of the continent can best be summarized by reference to these persistent elements: three geosynclines, three borderlands, and a low stable interior. In addition to these the Canadian Shield remained largely undisturbed from the Pre-Cambrian.

1. The *Appalachian geosyncline* occupied the approximate position and northeast trend of the present Appalachian folded mountains, connecting the Gulf of Mexico with the North Atlantic Ocean (Alabama to Newfoundland). A temporarily separated branch of this geosyncline is referred to as the *Acadian trough.* These downfolded zones received most of their substantial thicknesses of sediments from the erosion of the second feature, known as Appalachia.

2. *Appalachia* was an island arc, paralleling the Appalachian geosyncline on the site of the present Piedmont and Atlantic Coastal Plain, and extending an unknown distance eastward across the present continental shelf. An assemblage of shallow seas, deep basins, long troughs, and archipelagoes, it was an active zone marked by tectonic instability.

3. The *Cordilleran geosyncline* occupied a northward-trending zone between the present Rocky Mountains and the Pacific Coast states, connecting with the Pacific Ocean in southern California and extending north to the Arctic Ocean. It obtained most of its sediment from bordering lands on the west, known as Cascadia.

4. *Cascadia* extended along the Pacific Coast, including the site of the present Cascade and Coast ranges, and westward an uncertain distance into the Pacific Ocean.

5. The *Ouachita geosyncline* extended across Oklahoma, Texas,

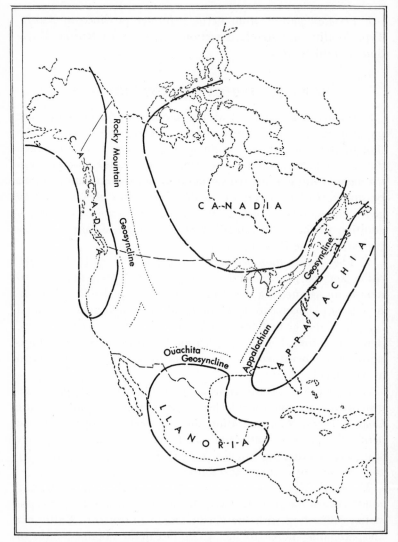

Fig. 40—Map of generalized land masses and geosynclines of Paleozoic North America. (By permission from *Introduction to College Geology*, by Chauncey D. Holmes, copyright 1949 by The Macmillan Co.)

and northern Mexico. It received its sediment from an adjacent borderland on the south, known as Llanoria.

6. *Llanoria,* extended from Arkansas across Louisiana and southern Texas to include most of Mexico and much of the northern part of the present Gulf of Mexico.

The borderlands rose from time to time as they were being eroded, as a result of which the rate of erosion and the deposition and character of the deposits in the adjacent sea varied throughout this long era. In complementary fashion, the geosynclines proceeded, with brief cessations and reversals, to sink as sediment accumulated in them. At certain times the three geosynclinal belts probably were in contact, surrounded by a continuous outer margin of highlands. Between the geosynclines was the seventh principal feature, the Interior Lowland.

7. *Interior Lowland, Central Lowland,* or *Interior Platform,* consisted of low plains situated in the heart of the continent and participated but little in the mobility that characterized the rest of the continent.

Paleozoic Cycles. Seven great episodes of inundation by the sea during the Paleozoic era correspond to the seven geologic periods. The water entered each time as narrow seaways along the geosynclines, spreading widely across the lower parts of the land, eventually separating the continent into a number of large islands. These oceanic invasions were slow and halting, three or more phases being recognized for each submergence. Thus, Early and Late, or Early, Middle, and Late *epochs* are distinguishable for each period; the corresponding groups of rocks are called the Lower and Upper, or the Lower, Middle, and Upper *series.* Each geologic period ended in a gradual but complete emergence of the continent, as the seas were drained back into the ocean basins. These times of emergence usually coincided with the rise of mountains, so that the breaks between periods were further accentuated. Toward the close of the Paleozoic, extensive swamps were formed, in which vegetation accumulated that would later become coal. The final (Permian) period was least typical, for the sea was by then confined to limited basins scattered from Mexico to Alaska.

Paleozoic Rocks. During each of the major subdivisions of the seven Paleozoic periods, a sequence of related rocks was deposited, chiefly of marine origin. These *series* in North America are generally named for the localities where they were first systematically studied. The following list gives them in order from oldest to youngest. Each of them embraces from one to many individual formations, some of which are well known and of considerable importance; space is not available to attempt to name any of the hundreds of American Paleozoic formations or their members.

Cambrian period
1. Waucoban
2. Albertan
3. Croixan

Ordovician period
4. Canadian
5. Champlainian
6. Cincinnatian

Silurian period
7. Medinan
8. Niagaran
9. Cayugan

Devonian period
10. Lower Devonian
11. Middle Devonian
12. Upper Devonian

Mississippian period
13. Waverlyan
14. Tennesseean

Pennsylvanian period
15. Lower Pennsylvanian
16. Middle Pennsylvanian
17. Upper Pennsylvanian

Permian period
18. Lower Permian
19. Middle Permian
20. Upper Permian

Paleozoic Mountains. Successive uplifts of the borderlands of North America during the Paleozoic era produced several generations of high mountains, as well as volcanic activity, around the rim of the continent. The era concluded with one of the most intense mountain-building events in geologic history.

TACONIC DISTURBANCE. The first of these orogenies was the *Taconic* or *Taconian disturbance* which took place in the Ordovician. Slowly, then with increasing rapidity, the northern part of Appalachia rose and was thrust westward. As part of this orogeny, sediments in the Appalachian geosyncline were folded as far west as the present Hudson River. Associated vulcanism occurred from Newfoundland to Pennsylvania and continued into the Silurian period, after the mountain-making had ceased. The belt of Taconic folding and thrusting extended from Nova Scotia to New Jersey.

ACADIAN DISTURBANCE. The uplift in northern Appalachia was renewed as the *Acadian disturbance* in the Devonian period, producing another range, even more extensive than the Taconic mountains. This, the Acadian Range, ran from Newfoundland as far south possibly as North Carolina. The Acadian orogeny, which also folded sediments in the Appalachian geosyncline and the related Acadian trough, was accompanied by much intrusive and extrusive igneous activity.

APPALACHIAN REVOLUTION. Intensive orogeny, beginning in the Mississippian period, reached its climax in the *Appalachian revolution* of the Permian period. The borderland of Appalachia was thrust northwestward, folding and crushing the sedimentary rocks of the Appalachian geosyncline into a major mountain chain that reached without interruption from Newfoundland to Alabama, and perhaps farther west. East of the folds and thrust faults, huge batholiths intruded to become the cores of the mountains. The structural features of the present Appalachian Mountains originated in this grand event.

OUACHITA DISTURBANCE. Movements in Arkansas, Oklahoma, and Texas, which raised Llanoria above the fast-subsiding Ouachita geosyncline, are of a related nature and may have been continuous with the Appalachian activity during the Mississippian and Pennsylvanian periods. The Arbuckle, Wichita, and Amarillo mountains (together known as the Oklahoma Mountains) rose during the Pennsylvanian period. Finally in the Permian period the entire Ouachita geosyncline was compressed from the southeast, resulting in the formation of the Ouachita Mountains. The orogeny which took place is referred to as the *Ouachita disturbance.*

ANCESTRAL ROCKY MOUNTAINS. Instability in Colorado and New Mexico from the Mississippian to the Permian periods terminated in the formation of the Colorado Mountains (commonly called the Ancestral Rockies) in those states and adjoining ones.

PACIFIC BORDER. Extensive vulcanism occurred in the Permian period in Alaska, western Idaho and eastern Oregon, eastern California and western Nevada, and central Mexico.

OTHER CONTINENTS. From the British Isles to Scandinavia, and possibly across the Arctic Ocean to northern Greenland, the *Caledonian disturbance* produced the Caledonian Mountains in the

Silurian period. Other Silurian mountains were formed from France to Austria, in North Africa, and in Siberia.

Igneous activity made its appearance in the British Isles during the Devonian period, and intensive Devonian mountain-building and widespread igneous action occurred in eastern Australia.

Much vulcanism marked the Mississippian period in Great Britain and on the Continent.

The Variscan Mountains, the "roots" of which can be seen across western Europe, were built during the last part of the Paleozoic. The Himalaya region underwent substantial orogeny in the Pennsylvanian period. The Ural Mountains and ranges along the Pacific coast of Asia were folded during the Permian period.

MINERAL RESOURCES

Coal is the most distinctive economic product of the Paleozoic era. In addition to its tremendous economic significance, the abundance of coal reflects the climatic and geologic conditions that prevailed throughout the latter part of the Paleozoic era.

Coal. Eighty per cent of the world's coal production, and a larger proportion of the highest-quality coal, comes from deposits of Pennsylvanian age in North America and Europe. The anthracite beds of eastern Pennsylvania are unequaled.

Salt. Widespread rock-salt deposits represent extreme evaporation during two periods in the Paleozoic: the Silurian (in New York, Pennsylvania, Ohio, Michigan, and Ontario) and the Permian (in Kansas, Oklahoma, Texas, and New Mexico).

Potash. Permian deposits in New Mexico and Texas contain vast reserves of potash, and there are similarly important deposits of potash and salt of the same age in Germany and Russia.

Iron. The Clinton iron ore of Alabama, which is Silurian in age, is one of the principal mineral resources of the United States.

Petroleum. Oil and natural gas of immense value come from strata of all the Paleozoic periods.

Stone. Building stones of many types and other construction materials of various kinds are recovered from Paleozoic rocks.

CLIMATE

In view of the length of time the Paleozoic era lasted, the climatic conditions were probably no more extreme than those of any other geologic interval. Certain features characteristic of the era furnish vivid pictures of the earth during that early time.

Coral. The widespread Paleozoic seas moderated the climate so that coral reefs developed even in Arctic seas, where they are now found in such places as Spitzbergen.

Swamps. The lush, coarsely cellular vegetation, abundant in the Mississippian and especially in the Pennsylvanian coal swamps in many parts of the world, indicates clearly the persistency of warm, moist climates during those periods.

Deserts. Inland sea deposits of salt and gypsum, as well as sandstone of dune origin, testify to the prolonged aridity in the Great Lakes region during the Silurian period. Salt, potash, gypsum, and anhydrite; sand dunes in the Permian Basin of New Mexico and Texas; dunes from an earlier basin in Oklahoma and Kansas —all indicate that a dry climate prevailed throughout the West. These dead seas and desert landscapes have their counterparts in the large Permian deposits in Germany and Russia.

Glaciation. During the Permian period there was extensive glaciation in the Southern Hemisphere. Parts of India were covered with continental glaciers. Evidence of glaciation is most impressive in South Africa, and Australia and South America were also heavily glaciated. The ice reached within 20 degrees of the equator in India and 10 degrees in Brazil.

PLANTS

At the beginning of the Paleozoic era, *algae* were virtually the sole representatives of the plant kingdom. Numerous kinds of algae abounded, among which were many species of *seaweed* that sheltered and fed the small invertebrates crowding the Paleozoic seas. Some Paleozoic formations are attributable to lime-secreting algae, although much of the Paleozoic limestone may also have been formed, as limestone is today, by the precipitating action of *bacteria*.

Moss, lichen, and other primitive plants may have grown on land in moist, protected places even before the Cambrian period, but it was the development of vascular plants in the Devonian period that made possible the emancipation of plant life from a watery habitat. Having woody fibers for the circulation of fluids, these plants spread rapidly over the continents with conspicuous success, opening a whole new course to the processes of evolution.

A luxuriant flora is the distinguishing characteristic of the Coal Measures (the coal-bearing sediments) of the Pennsylvanian period, when small plants evolved to tree size and were virtually world-wide in distribution. Throughout this period primitive tree ferns were common, reaching heights of 50 feet, with 6-foot fronds. *Seed ferns,* bearing seeds instead of spores, may have been the precursors of all the higher seed-bearing plants. *Scouring rushes,* especially those of the genus *Calamites,* grew to great dimensions and were characterized by ribbed and jointed woody stems surrounding a core of pith. The *scale trees* stood in extraordinary profusion. Two types were dominant: *Lepidodendron,* whose diamond-shaped leaf scars were arranged in spiral rows on a corklike bark, and *Sigillaria,* marked by vertical rows of leaf scars. The *Cordaites,* forerunners of the *conifers,* exhibited long, bladelike leaves and bore seeds in racemes instead of cones. True conifers appeared toward the end of Paleozoic time.

ANIMALS

The remains of reasonably complex animal life appear first in geologic order in lower Cambrian strata. However, this fact does not signify that higher forms simply sprang up full-fledged within that period. On the contrary, so large and diversified a population could not have occurred without a long period of evolution, during which sufficient time elapsed for some animals to become encased in armor, such as shells, for protection against other newly established carnivorous forms.

Marine Invertebrates. In sharp contrast to the scanty fossil record of the Pre-Cambrian eras, the Paleozoic seas were crowded from earliest Cambrian time with invertebrates of many kinds. One of the most distinctive creatures was the *trilobite,* an *arachnid* with three major body divisions (head, thorax, and tail), and three segments widthwise, presenting a "tri-lobed" appearance. The trilobites dominated Cambrian and Ordovician seas, dying out by the end of the Permian period. A tiny relative of the trilobite is the *ostracod,* a bean-shaped *crustacean* which appeared in the Ordovician and is represented among modern fauna.

Gastropod mollusks originated in the Cambrian period, and

so also did the *cephalopods,* whose *nautiloids* and now extinct *ammonoids* remain some of the most useful index fossils of that period, though their climax came later in the Mesozoic. *Pelecypods* evolved in the Ordovician, and *brachiopods,* not true mollusks, though having, like clams, a two-part shell, originated in the Cambrian and were the most abundant shellfish in the Paleozoic seas.

Two main types of *corals,* the *tabulate* and the *rugose,* thrived during the Paleozoic, and left reefs in many parts of the world. *Bryozoan* colonies also accumulated to form reefs. Stalked *echinoderms* were numerous, particularly *crinoids* and *blastoids.*

Graptolites, foraminifera, and *radiolarians* are among the most important index fossils of the Paleozoic, occurring in widespread areas and only in specific strata.

Land Invertebrates. Land-living invertebrates are generally scarce in Paleozoic rocks. Spiders, scorpions, and millipedes—all *arthropods*—are abundant, however, in certain coal-bearing beds of the Pennsylvanian period. *Insects* originated in the Devonian period and increased in number and size during the Pennsylvanian period, the greatest having a wingspread of 29 inches.

Vertebrates. The earliest known vertebrate remains occur in Ordovician rocks. These are the *Ostracoderms,* primitive jawless and limbless fishes which probably originated in fresh water. By Devonian time numerous groups of fish were occupying both marine and fresh-water habitats. The *Placoderms* include a large number of diverse fish types, all of which have paired fins and some sort of structure resembling a jaw. The *Chondrichthyes,* cartilagenous fishes embracing sharks, skates, and rays, evolved in marine waters and have highly developed jaws and fins. Some of the Paleozoic sharks attained the largest size (20 feet) of any Paleozoic animal.

The bony fishes evolved in fresh water, diverging into two important groups: the *ray-finned* fishes, which today are represented by all the common fishes; and the *Choanichthyes* (fish with internal nostrils), represented by the *lungfish* (of which some rare forms exist today) and the *crossopterygian* fish (whose bony, lobed fin structure and breathing apparatus suggest a taxonomic position ancestral to land vertebrates).

Paleozoic *amphibians* (called *stegocephalians* because of their bony skull plates) probably evolved from crossopterygian forms in the Devonian period. Though able to travel successfully on land, these animals, like all amphibians, were bound to the water, their life cycle requiring a liquid environment for the development of the eggs and young. Later in the Paleozoic, *reptiles* completed the transition to land. Evolving from the amphibians in the Carboniferous period, they developed an egg whose shell and inner membranes afforded an ideal environment for the maturation of young out of the water.

REVIEW QUESTIONS

1. Name in order the periods of the Paleozoic era.
2. What periods are included in the Carboniferous interval?
3. Identify and locate the Appalachian, Cordilleran, and Ouachita geosynclines.
4. Identify and locate Appalachia, Cascadia, and Llanoria.
5. What was the geologic function of the Interior Lowland?
6. Give the history of the following orogenies: Taconic disturbance, Acadian disturbance, Appalachian revolution, Ouachita disturbance, Caledonian disturbance.
7. Name the principal mineral resources of the Paleozoic era.
8. What climatic significance does each of the following have: Paleozoic coral, Pennsylvanian coal swamps, Silurian deserts, Permian glaciation?
9. Describe the vegetation of the Pennsylvanian period.
10. What were the leading marine invertebrates of the Paleozoic era?
11. Describe the vertebrates of the Devonian period.

23

Mesozoic Era

The Mesozoic era (era of "middle life") is divided into three periods. These are, beginning with the oldest, as follows:

1. *Triassic period,* so called from its threefold (*trias,* three) nature in central Germany. Type locality, Germany; standard section, Alps. Duration; 49 million years.

2. *Jurassic period,* from the Jura Alps, mostly between France and Switzerland. Type locality, Jura Mountains; standard section, Jura Mountains and England. Duration 46 million years.

3. *Cretaceous period,* from the chalk deposits of the English Channel. Type locality and standard section, west-central Europe. Duration, 72 million years.

LANDS AND SEAS

The dominant physical features of North America during the Mesozoic era were related to their Paleozoic predecessors; the Canadian Shield maintained its stability as before.

1. The *Appalachian Mountains,* with today's structures formed by the close of the Permian period, occupied the former site of the Appalachian geosyncline, from which they were derived.

2. *Appalachia,* a high island-arc borderland in the previous era, gradually foundered during the Mesozoic and was flooded by the waters of the Atlantic Ocean along the Atlantic Coastal Plain.

3. The *Interior Lowland* continued as a stable central plain surrounded by mountains and troughs on the east, south, and west.

4. The *Ouachita Mountains* bordered the Interior Lowland on the south in the region of the former Ouachita geosyncline and were at times continuous with the Appalachian Mountains.

5. *Llanoria,* the former borderland along the United States-Mexico boundary, subsided into the Gulf of Mexico during the Mesozoic era and was invaded by ocean waters.

6. The *Rocky Mountain geosyncline,* changing considerably

in size, shape, and position during the Mesozoic era, replaced the Ancestral Rockies and eventually became a vast seaway approximately 500 to 1,000 miles wide, extending from the Gulf of Mexico to the Arctic Ocean. The southern part is known as the *Mexican geosyncline.*

7. The *Columbian trough,* a geosyncline, occupied Alaska, Yukon Territory, and British Columbia. It later rose to become part of the:

8. *Mesocordilleran geanticline,* a narrow zone of highlands running from Alaska to Mexico. It furnished sediments to the adjacent subsiding geosynclines east and west of it.

9. The *California trough* was a geosyncline lying in a northwestward direction along the Pacific Coast states and at times joining one or both of the other western troughs in an enlarged seaway. When merged with the Columbian trough, the two are referred to as the *Pacific Coast geosyncline.*

10. *Cascadia,* a marginal highland along the Pacific Coast, and various island borderlands of unknown size derived from the Pacific Coast geosyncline lay between this geosyncline and the Pacific Ocean.

Mesozoic Cycles. Three major episodes of marine invasion of North America, corresponding to the three geologic periods, occurred during the Mesozoic era. During the Cretaceous period there was a general sinking of lowlands; the sea advanced from the directions of Alaska and the Gulf of Mexico, bisecting the continent in the middle of the period. Toward the end of the Cretaceous, broad areas of coal swamps were formed in the West, analogous to those existing in the East in the preceding era.

Mesozoic Rocks. The Mesozoic rock series in North America are named simply Lower, Middle, and Upper, for both the Triassic period and the Jurassic period. Cretaceous rocks are divided into a Lower (or *Comanchean series*) and Upper (or *Gulfian series*), but three natural divisions are found in Mexico and southern Europe; hence Mexican and European nomenclature does not correspond to ours. These series are subdivided into hundreds of formations.

Mesozoic Mountains. Each of the three periods of the Mesozoic era was marked by a significant orogeny, largely confined to its own region. The last of these, accompanied by large-scale igneous activity, was one of the most notable revolutions in earth history.

PALISADIAN DISTURBANCE. At the end of the Triassic (and probably continuing into the Jurassic) period, the Appalachian Mountains between Nova Scotia and North Carolina were affected by the *Palisadian* disturbance, which uplifted and dislocated the rocks by faulting them into a chain of block mountains. Earlier in the Triassic a number of troughs (graben) known as the "Newark basins" had formed in the same region; these had been partially filled with red sediment and basaltic lava flows and sills, and were then involved in the Palisadian disturbance.

NEVADIAN DISTURBANCE. Late in the Jurassic period, forces from the west folded the sediments in the Columbian and California geosynclines into a mountain chain which extended from California and Nevada to British Columbia. This intense orogeny is known as the *Nevadian disturbance;* it involved the intrusion of the huge Coast Range and Sierra Nevada batholiths and much volcanic activity.

LARAMIDE REVOLUTION. Intensive folding took place in the Rocky Mountain geosyncline toward the end of the Cretaceous period. Continuing into the Cenozoic era, it produced most of the present structure of the Rocky Mountains. The compression was directed from the northwest, so that in general the Northern Rockies are strongly overthrust, the Middle Rockies less complexly faulted, and the Southern Rockies merely thrown into open folds consisting of alternating mountain ranges and valleys, or "parks." Vulcanism was a conspicuous accompaniment of this Laramide revolution, and the Idaho batholith and associated igneous bodies were intruded.

OTHER CONTINENTS. Large-scale intrusive and extrusive vulcanism occurred in South Africa during the Triassic period.

Corresponding to the Rocky Mountain geosyncline was the *Andean geosyncline,* which was folded at the end of the Cretaceous period into the Andes Mountains, extending the full length of South America. Transverse to both Rockies and Andes is the Antillean mountain chain of Central America and the West Indies, which was formed at the same time.

MINERAL RESOURCES

The geologic conditions of the Mesozoic era created a vast amount of mineral wealth.

Coal. Jurassic and Cretaceous coal, especially the latter, is distributed from Antarctica to Spitzbergen and constitutes enormous reserves in western North America, though mostly of poor quality.

Petroleum. Cretaceous and other Mesozoic rocks are among the leading sources of oil and natural gas.

Gold. In the western foothills of the Sierra Nevada is the Mother Lode belt of California, one of the world's richest gold-producing areas. The gold was deposited in quartz veins in the Jurassic period.

Other Metals. Silver, copper, lead, and zinc mineralization related to the Laramide revolution occurs throughout the Rocky Mountains and the Great Basin region.

CLIMATE

The elevation of mountains in the Nevadian disturbance and the Laramide revolution brought colder and drier climates on a regional scale, which were moderated as erosion reduced the average altitude of the land and the oceans spread widely over the continents.

Deserts. Large deposits of dune sand as well as beds of gypsum and other evaporation products indicate desert conditions in the West during the first half of the Mesozoic. In the Triassic period aridity was widespread in South America, western Europe, and South Africa. Dryness is clearly evident, also, in southeastern United States during the later part of the era.

Swamps. The second half of the Mesozoic produced a strikingly different climate, indicated by thick coal beds and abundant remains of swamp-inhabiting dinosaurs in many parts of the world. Warm temperatures and high humidity prevailed.

Glaciation. A brief interval of refrigeration, at least in eastern Australia, produced glaciers in that region during the Cretaceous.

PLANTS

With the extinction of most of the Paleozoic flora, the vegetation at the beginning of the Mesozoic era consisted largely of *evergreen trees;* these were mainly *conifers* and the peculiar *gingko,* thriving with *cycadeoid palms* above an undergrowth of *ferns* and *scouring rushes.*

A notable change in the flora of the earth took place in the

Cretaceous period, when new types of plants made their appearance. *Deciduous* trees, with net-veined leaves, spread rapidly and gave a modern look to the landscape, mixed though they were with conifers such as the *sequoia*. Most of the deciduous trees were then, as now, *angiosperms* ("enclosed seeds"), the highest type of plants, including all true flowering plants. These were to supply fruits, nuts, grasses, cereals, and vegetables for the more advanced forms of animal life that were due shortly to come upon the scene.

ANIMALS

The Mesozoic era is often referred to as the Age of Reptiles, or the Age of Dinosaurs, for among the dinosaurs were the largest and most ferocious reptiles. Certain invertebrate animals, however, shared the Mesozoic stage and ruled the seas as completely as the dinosaurs held sway upon the land.

Invertebrates. The most conspicuous invertebrates of the Mesozoic era were the *ammonites*. Practically all were coiled, occupying, thin, pearly, and sutured shells of considerable beauty. *Belemnites,* cigar-shaped mollusks resembling squids, were another major kind of shellfish abundant in the Mesozoic. Besides these now extinct groups, there were many other invertebrates similar to those that live today, such as lobsters, shrimp, crabs, clams, snails, and modern corals.

Mesozoic insects were abundant, and most of the modern orders were represented.

Reptiles. Mesozoic reptiles expanded dramatically and adapted themselves to land, sea, and air.

DINOSAURS. The most distinctive Mesozoic animals were the two orders of dinosaurs, presumably descended from Triassic reptiles known as thecodonts. All were adapted for running, but in other ways they differed from each other greatly. Most dinosaurs were herbivorous, but some were carnivorous; most were bipedal and ran on two feet like ostriches, but others moved more deliberately on four heavy limbs. They lived in forests, on plains, in rivers, lakes, and swamps. The monstrous dinosaurs so exciting to the layman (the word *dinosaur* means in Greek "terrible lizard") evolved from early ones of small size, and some species never grow larger than a rooster.

Dinosaurs may be divided into the order *Saurischia,* characterized by a lizardlike pelvic and hip structure and the order *Ornithischia,* having birdlike hips or pelvis.

1. The *Saurischian dinosaurs* are divided into the *Theropoda* and the *Sauropoda.*

The Theropods included all bipedal forms, mainly carnivorous in habit. *Allosaurus,* with claws and teeth shaped for tearing flesh, was a powerful creature, and the formidable *Tyrannosaurus* was the largest meat-eater that ever lived.

The Sauropods—quadrupedal, herbivorous, and amphibious—were the largest of the dinosaurs; *Brontosaurus* was the best-known giant of this kind, attaining a length of 67 feet and weighing 30 tons; *Diplodocus* was more slender and even longer, reaching a record 87½ feet.

2. The *Ornithischian dinosaurs* included four principal types, all herbivores, having blunt nails and using their back teeth to feed on plants.

Of the bipedal forms, the "duck-billed dinosaur" *Trachodon* is a striking example.

The "plated dinosaurs" are represented by *Stegosaurus,* clumsy but dangerous, with a double row of protective plates and spines down his back and a knob of spikes at the end of his tail.

The "armored dinosaurs," typified by *Ankylosaurus,* were thoroughly clad for battle.

One of the "horned dinosaurs" was *Triceratops,* also built for defense, with three horns on a huge head and a bony extension of the skull protecting the neck; *Protoceratops* is the horned dinosaur whose eggs have been found in Mongolia.

FLYING REPTILES. Some Mesozoic reptiles flew or glided through the air. The wings of the *pterodactyls* were supported by a greatly elongated finger, while the other digits served as claws. *Pteranodon* was the largest flying animal known, having a wingspread of 24 feet.

SWIMMING REPTILES. Four orders of reptiles took to the ocean. (1) *Turtles* are still numerous; the other groups became extinct at the end of the Mesozoic era. (2) *Ichthyosaurs,* resembling dolphins and highly streamlined, grew to a length of 25 feet. (3) *Mosasaurs,* also streamlined, were characterized by scaly skin and vicious teeth in powerful jaws. (4) *Plesiosaurs,* some of which were as much as 50 feet long, had elongated necks and large flippers, with which they paddled through the water.

Birds. The first bird, *Archaeopteryx,* is found in Jurassic rocks. Although clothed in feathers, it had teeth, clawed wings, and a long tail, indicating a close relationship to the thecodont reptiles. Cretaceous birds included *Ichthyornis* and *Hesperornis,* the last a huge diving bird at home in the water and unable to fly.

Mammals. The first mammals (warm-blooded animals that suckle their young) evolved from small mammal-like reptiles in the Jurassic. *Insectivores* (nocturnal, insect-eating mammals, represented by today's moles, shrews, and hedgehogs) and *marsupials* (pouch-bearing mammals, such as modern opossums and kangaroos) were more advanced forms living in the Mesozoic era. They had specialized teeth and showed signs of acquiring versatile habits, but their day had not yet come.

REVIEW QUESTIONS

1. Name in chronological order the periods of the Mesozoic era.
2. Identify and locate the Rocky Mountain geosyncline, Columbian trough, California trough, and Pacific Coast geosyncline.
3. Identify and locate the Mesocordilleran geanticline.
4. Give the history of the following orogenies: Palisade disturbance, Nevadian disturbance, Laramide revolution.
5. What was distinctive about the climates of the Mesozoic era?
6. Name the chief plants of the Mesozoic era?
7. Describe the ammonites.
8. Describe the following dinosaurs: Allosaurus, Tyrannosaurus, Brontosaurus, Diplodocus, Trachodon, Stegosaurus, Ankylosaurus, Triceratops, and Protoceratops.
9. Describe the pterodactyls.
10. Name the four kinds of swimming reptiles.
11. Describe two forms of Mesozoic mammals.

24

Cenozoic Era

The earth has acquired its present topography during the last, relatively short era of geologic time (about 63 million years). The features of its landscape, the shapes of the continents, the courses of the rivers, the climatic zones, the distribution of plants and animals—all have been established within the Cenozoic era. Not only has superficial sculpturing taken place, but also great structural events have occurred: the Himalaya and the Alps have risen from the bottom of the sea, and the Rocky Mountains and other ranges have been worn down and uplifted at least once. The processes of geology are continuous; as the mountains have risen, agents of erosion have sculptured their surfaces.

CENOZOIC PERIODS AND EPOCHS

The Cenozoic era (era of "recent life") is unequally divided into two periods, the Tertiary and the Quaternary, the latter covering the last million years. (The names themselves are not meaningful today, being relics of an early classification of the earth's rock bodies.)

The Tertiary period is subdivided into five epochs, the names of which end in *-cene* (Greek = recent), referring to forms of life —originally to the percentage of still-living shelled invertebrate species found in each series of rocks. The assemblage of fossils, recording major oscillations of land and sea, is now the criterion for dating Tertiary rocks. The following represent the approximate lengths of the subdivisions of Tertiary time.

1. *Paleocene* ("ancient recent") *epoch*. Duration, 5 million years.

2. *Eocene* ("dawn recent") *epoch*. Duration, 22 million years.

3. *Oligocene* ("little recent") *epoch*. Duration, 11 million years.

4. *Miocene* ("less recent") *epoch*. Duration, 12 million years.

5. *Pliocene* ("more recent") *epoch*. Duration 12 million years.

The type locality of the Tertiary period is the Paris Basin in France.

The Quaternary period is divided into two epochs:

1. *Pleistocene* ("most recent") *epoch,* synonymous with the Ice Age. Duration, approximately 1 million years.

2. *Recent epoch,* since the start of the last retreat of the glaciers, about 11,000 years ago.

The Pleistocene is a very short segment of the Cenozoic era, characterized only by a different climate; the Recent epoch, in which we live, has also occupied but a brief span of geologic history. The Quaternary has slight status in the geologic time scale; but it is of the greatest significance to us because it is the period in which man has flourished.

The terms Paleogene and Neogene are gradually superseding Tertiary and Quaternary, respectively, though not as exact equivalents. The Paleogene system corresponds to the Paleocene to Oligocene epochs; the Neogene system, to the Miocene to Pleistocene epochs.

PHYSICAL HISTORY

Except for a short interval during which the oceans reached the interior by way of the Mississippi Valley and made a brief stand in the Dakotas, North America has been inundated only along the margins of the continent since the Cretaceous period. Hence, tracing the changing pattern of lands and seas, so vital to the study of past eras, is no longer applicable to the study of Cenozoic geology. Instead, the events of the Cenozoic era are best summarized by discussing them from the standpoint of the major physical subdivisions of the continent, since the existing relief features of the earth were largely developed during this era.

Atlantic Coast. The Atlantic coastal plain, from Long Island to Florida, was partly submerged during the early Tertiary but gradually rose from beneath the water. Florida was a shallow submarine bank during most of the Cenozoic.

Gulf Coast. The Gulf coastal plain, from Florida to Yucatan, was occupied by the sea in a broad, curving band, which extended inland up the Mississippi Valley nearly to St. Louis. The river and its tributaries imposed a swampy topography upon much of the southern coastal region in the United States. As the Mississippi delta grew seaward to its present position, the bottom of the Gulf of Mexico subsided rapidly under its heavy load of sediment, creating a trough referred to as the *Gulf Coast geosyncline,* which parallels the shoreline of Louisiana and Mississippi.

Plugs of rock salt, forced upward into the overlying strata, are a distinctive feature of Gulf Coast structure, and are known as *salt domes.*

Appalachian Mountains. With the exception of the Great Smokies and scattered peaks in New England, the Appalachian Mountains were thoroughly eroded by the beginning of the Tertiary period. During the Cenozoic era they were warped slowly upward into a low arch, and the Paleozoic structures were carved by geologic agents into their present relief. Three main erosion surfaces—the highest and oldest, *Schooley peneplain,* the *Harrisburg erosion surface,* and the *Somerville erosion surface*—record the history of this region.

Interior Lowland. Overlapping the Canadian Shield, with which they combined to make a central stable region, the rocks of the interior of the continent formed a lowland between the Appalachian Mountains and the western Great Plains. The High Plains east of the Rockies received much sediment from the Rocky Mountains.

Rocky Mountains. Large structural basins in the Rocky Mountain region produced by the Laramide orogeny represent downfolded areas between the uparched mountain ranges which stood high at the beginning of the Tertiary period. Into these basins was deposited the sediment eroded from the mountains, which were slowly cut down to about the level of the filling basins to make a wide, flat surface of combined erosion and deposition. Substantial uplift during the last part of the Tertiary raised the Rockies again to mountainous heights, and their forms were sculptured anew by rejuvenated streams, which hollowed out the former basins. Two main erosion surfaces, the *Flattop peneplain* and the *Rocky Mountain peneplain,* indicate the sequence of uplift and erosion in these mountains.

Colorado Plateau. This plateau region lies in the American Southwest—in Arizona, Utah, New Mexico, and Colorado. Repeated uplift during the Cenozoic era arched the Mesozoic rocks of this region into a broad dome several thousand feet above sea level. As erosion stripped away a considerable portion of these comparatively horizontal formations, a spectacular series of step-like cliffs was formed as a result of the alternation of hard and soft beds that characterizes the sequence. Continued uplift rejuvenated the rivers, which proceeded to incise canyons of profound depth. One of these is the Grand Canyon, carved by the Colorado River and over a mile deep.

Basin and Range Province. The Basin and Range province occupies the central part of the mid-Cordilleran region of the United States. Its north-trending mountains are tilted fault blocks of Tertiary origin. They are surrounded by wide, flat-bottomed desert valleys filled with sediments, which have piled up to such an extent that some of the isolated mountains are fairly well buried in their own debris.

Columbia Plateau. Between the Northern Rocky Mountains and the Cascade Range are enormous lava flows which flooded the pre-existing relief and built up a vast warped upland known as the Columbia Plateau. The flows were fissure eruptions of basalt extruded in the Cenozoic era.

Pacific Coast. The Cenozoic history of the Pacific coastal region is very complex. The physical features comprise a series of mountain chains and structural basins. As the mountains rose, the basins sank, forming a number of isolated areas of sedimentation. An enormous fault block over five hundred miles in length was tilted westward. The eastern elevated edge of this block forms the Sierra Nevada; the western depressed side underlies the Great Valley of California. In line with the Sierra Nevada, the Cascade Range extends from northern California through Oregon and Washington to British Columbia. The Great Valley of California lies between the similarly placed basins of the Gulf of California and Puget Sound. The Coast Ranges are a composite of mountains running from Baja California to Alaska.

The Pacific Northwest. During the Cenozoic era the western half of North America was the scene of a powerful crustal movement, known as the *Cascadian orogeny*, which was accompanied by extreme volcanic activity. A granite batholith was intruded into the Cascade Range, the Coast Ranges and Puget Sound basin were folded, and the western mountains in general were vigorously uplifted and faulted. Vulcanism built up the Absaroka Range and Plateau in the Yellowstone Park region, the San Juan Mountains of southwestern Colorado, and the vast lava-covered Columbia-Snake River plateau, and crowned the Cascade Range with a series of mighty volcanoes extending from Mount

Shasta in northern California to Mount Baker in northern Washington.

Other Continents. The Andes, like the Rockies, were first eroded and then uplifted during the Cenozoic era. The Alps, the Himalaya, the Pyrenees, the Apennines, and the Carpathians were pushed up to their present heights. Other important mountain ranges of the world were likewise created by the Cenozoic orogeny. Most of the world's mountains involved in the Cenozoic orogenies seem to be still rising. Vulcanism was widespread in the West Indian Arc, the North Atlantic (Azores, Iceland), in East Africa, the Mediterranean, the Near East and elsewhere. However, it reached its culmination in the "circle of fire" around the Pacific Ocean, which in the New World includes the volcanic belts of the Andes, Central America, Mexico, the Cascades in the western United States, the coast ranges of southern Alaska, and the Aleutian Islands.

MINERAL RESOURCES

Cenozoic mineral products, especially petroleum and metals, are of substantial value.

Coal. Tertiary coal, though considerable in amount, is too recently formed to be of much commercial value except when metamorphosed. It is marketed chiefly west of the Cascade and Sierra Nevada ranges.

Petroleum. Nearly all the rich oil fields (in California, along the Gulf Coast, in Venezuela, Baku, and Rumania, and along the Persian Gulf) are in Tertiary rocks. The Green River Basin in Wyoming and Colorado is noted for its thick accumulation of Eocene *oil shale,* which may be regarded as a mineral resource of potentially immense value for the future.

Gold. Uplift of the Sierra Nevada resulted in erosion of the Mother Lode gold veins and deposition of Californian and Peruvian gold placers. There are important gold veins of Tertiary age at Cripple Creek, Colorado, and Goldfield, Nevada.

Other Metals. Tertiary igneous intrusions account for a large portion of the mineral wealth of the Rocky Mountains and Latin America. Silver deposits at Park City, Utah; at Tonopah, Nevada; of the Comstock Lode at Virginia City, Nevada; and in Mexico and Bolivia date from the Tertiary period. The huge copper mines of Bingham Canyon, Utah, and similar "porphyry copper" mines throughout the Western Hemisphere are also Tertiary deposits.

TERTIARY CLIMATE

The high elevations existing at the beginning of the Tertiary period were conducive to a varied climate throughout the world, but there was no glaciation as had previously been thought.

In contrast, a warm and moist climate prevailed uniformly over much of the earth during the first half of the Tertiary, as indicated by the northward spread of both animals and plants.

However, the climate became more diversified as the mountains rose, and the progressive cooling that took place in the last half of the period presaged the coming of the Ice Age in the Quaternary.

PLEISTOCENE GLACIATION

Brought into being by a combination of lowered average annual temperature and increased humidity, the glaciers of the Pleistocene found a variable topography upon which to operate—high and rugged in certain regions, low and with slight relief in others. Originating in elevated areas in higher latitudes and spreading over the adjoining terrain, *continental glaciers* expanded until they covered about one-fifth the land surface of the earth. Complementing them were *valley glaciers* moving amidst the lofty peaks of many mountain ranges even in equatorial regions. Some of the valley glaciers merged at the base of the range to form *piedmont glaciers*.

Chronology. *Multiple glaciation,* with alternating glacial and interglacial times, has been proved for the Pleistocene epoch by these lines of evidence:

1. Weathered glacial drift including gumbotil underneath fresh drift, indicating an interval of exposure between advances of the ice. *Gumbotil* is dark, sticky subsoil produced from till by weathering.

2. Fossils of plants and animals typical of mild climates, in deposits between separate layers of drift.

3. Analysis of pollen preserved in peat associated with glacial

deposits, furnishes information on the assemblages of trees growing at various times in given places.

4. Deposits of loess blown by wind upon ice-free ground during the recession of a glacier.

Four main *glacial stages* and three *interglacial stages* are recorded, based on a study of the character and relations of the glacial deposits, combined with radiocarbon age determinations. In order of occurrence they are named, in North America, as follows:

1. *Nebraskan Glacial Stage.* Largest exposure of glacial drift of this age is in Missouri; began about 1 million years ago; duration, 100,000 years.

2. *Aftonian Interglacial Stage.* Gumbotil formed by prolonged weathering of the Nebraskan drift 8 feet thick; duration, 200,000 years.

3. *Kansan Glacial Stage.* Largest exposure in Iowa; duration, 100,000 years.

4. *Yarmouthian Interglacial Stage.* Kansan drift deeply weathered, gumbotil 11 feet thick; duration, 310,000 years.

5. *Illinoian Glacial Stage.* Best represented in Illinois; mostly silt and clay; original relief reduced; duration, 100,000 years.

6. *Sangamonian Interglacial Stage.* Illinoian drift oxidized 10–25 feet deep, gumbotil formed by weathering of Illinoian drift 4–6 feet thick; duration, 135,000 years.

7. *Wisconsinan Glacial Stage.* Covers earlier glacial deposits except in central states, where its terminal moraines stretch across country in great loops that fall short of drift from other stages; mostly sand, gravel, and boulders; slight weathering, little eroded, physiographic features well preserved in Recent epoch; duration, 50,000–70,000 years. Divided in 1960 into five *substages* (earliest first):

1. Altonian	3. Woodfordian	5. Valderan
2. Farmdalian	4. Twocreekan	

Distribution. Four principal units of continental glaciation existed during the Pleistocene, as follows:

1. The *Laurentide ice sheet* centering over the Hudson Bay region of northeastern Canada. It eventually covered most of Canada east of the Rockies and the northeastern United States as far south as the present Missouri and Ohio rivers, and reached

the Atlantic from Long Island to Cape Cod. It joined the *Greenland ice sheet,* most of which still remains. Subsidiary centers of accumulation may have formed, as in Newfoundland. The curious "Driftless area" of Wisconsin, Illinois, and Iowa was surrounded by ice, but escaped being glaciated.

2. The *Scandinavian ice sheet,* covering all of Scandinavia, northern Germany, the Netherlands, western Russia, and almost all of the British Isles.

3. The *Siberian ice sheet.*

4. The *Antarctic ice sheet,* still remaining.

In addition, the Cordilleran region of western America and most of the other high mountains of the world were heavily glaciated—particularly the Alps, the Himalaya, the Caucasus, the Andes, Patagonia, and South Island in New Zealand.

The direction of movement of the glaciers is determined by mapping (1) the end moraines, (2) the orientation of glacial striae (scratches), and (3) the distribution of distinctive boulders (*erratics*), which can be traced to their source.

Effects. The profound effects of Pleistocene glaciation have thoroughly changed the face of much of our planet and still influence in some measure all present-day life in the following ways.

Climate. The glaciers, which resulted from a cooler and moister climate, help to prolong those conditions and thereby influence the present climate of the entire world.

Sea Level. The fall of sea level is correlated with the expansion of huge bodies of ice on the land, and the rise of sea level corresponds to their melting. These changes affect the gradients of streams and so intensify erosion (with falling sea level) or cause excessive deposition (with rising sea level). Land bridges, submarine canyons, coral reefs, and shoreline terraces are among the geologic features closely involved in the changing level of the ocean.

Soil. No effects of Pleistocene glaciation are more important than those concerning the soils of the Northern Hemisphere. In North America, for instance, the mantle has been stripped away from a vast territory in the Canadian Shield, leaving barren bedrock; father south are endless boulder fields, such as litter the ground in New England and make farming difficult; and elsewhere are the fine, fresh glacial deposits that provide a superlative soil, such as that of the wheat and corn lands of the central states and the Mississippi Valley region.

STREAM COURSES. Disrupting the drainage of the areas they invaded, the glaciers blocked or obliterated stream channels on a wholesale scale, turning the stream waters into new channels.

LAKES AND SWAMPS. Vast areas of swampland and a large majority of the world's lakes owe their origin to Pleistocene glaciation, which has superimposed a new, deranged drainage system upon the pre-existing terrain.

The Great Lakes. The basins occupied by the Great Lakes of North America, the world's largest chain of inland waterways, were widened and deepened to their present massive proportions by the erosive action of lobes of the Laurentide ice sheet, which scoured out the broad structural lowlands which had already been eroded by preglacial streams. The effect was most pronounced in the Superior and Michigan basins where the ice moved in the same direction as the trend of the depressions.

When the ice later retreated toward the north, a changing sequence of temporary lakes was left between the higher moraine-rimmed belt to the south and the front of the glacier to the north. This sequence of lakes occupied basins resulting from the scouring out and deepening of pre-existing valleys by the glacier, the blocking of preglacial stream channels by morainal deposition, and the downwarping of the earth's crust beneath the load of ice. Gradually the land recovered its earlier elevation, as is shown by the tilting of old lake shorelines (*strand lines*). These shorelines are elevated north of the *"hingle line"* (technically, the *zero isobase*) which extends southeastward from Michigan through southern Ontario and swings northeastward to Nova Scotia. This slow and complex uplift forced the drainage to seek various outlets, so that at different times in the past the Great Lakes have drained out in different directions. The Mississippi and Hudson-Mohawk valleys were among the outlets for the Great Lake drainage prior to the time that the present Niagara-St. Lawrence route was established.

Lake Agassiz. The largest of all known glacial lakes was Lake Agassiz. It was a shallow body of water covering an area five times that of Lake Superior and greater than that of all the Great Lakes put together. This lake was impounded by the ice sheet while it still occupied the Hudson Bay region. The ice front dammed the north-flowing stream channels in northern Ontario and Manitoba, producing an immense body of water which found an outlet southward through the Minnesota River, thence to the Mississippi. The existing remnants of Lake Agassiz include Lake Winnipeg, Lake Manitoba, and Lake of the Woods. The vast flat silt-covered former·lake bottom provides some of the continent's most fertile wheat-growing land today.

Lake Bonneville. The Pleistocene forerunner of Great Salt Lake, Utah, is known to geologists as Lake Bonneville. It attained a large size during the humid (*pluvial*) intervals in the now arid West, when it overflowed northward into the Snake and Columbia rivers. Finally, it shrank and the fresh water became saturated with sodium chloride and other salts. Glacial *Lake Lahontan,* of which Pyramid Lake in Nevada is a remnant, was another large pluvial Pleistocene lake in the same region. Idaho, Washington, and California contained other extensive lakes during the Ice Age.

PLANTS

The most significant event in the Cenozoic record of the plant kingdom took place in the Miocene epoch, when grasses spread quickly over the land. Cereals and grains not only covered the prairies and reduced the rate of erosion in a large part of the earth, but they also provided essential food for the new animal forms that were soon to make their appearance.

ANIMALS

The Cenozoic era is rightly called the Age of Mammals. With the extinction of the dinosaurs at the end of the Cretaceous, these new vertebrates rose vigorously from an insignificant status to their present dominance.

Invertebrates. Many kinds of invertebrate animals persisted from previous eras. Of especial interest among the invertebrates of the Tertiary are the *nummulites,* large coin-shaped *foraminifers* (protozoans having pores in 'their shells), enormously abundant in the ancestral Mediterranean waters, which occupied southern Europe, northern Africa, southwest Asia, and the Himalayan region. Nummulitic limestones many hundred feet thick occur in this region; from them the Pyramids of Egypt were built.

SOME TYPICAL FOSSILS

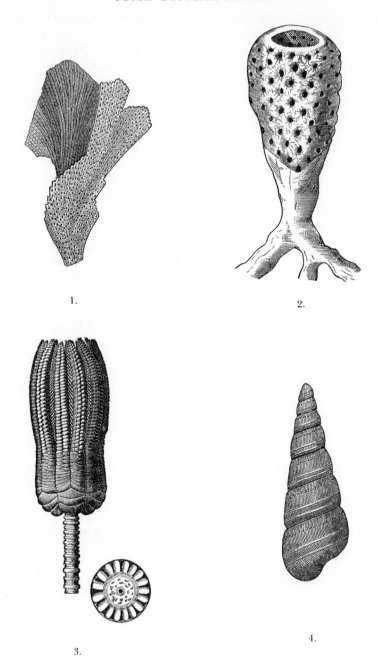

FIG. 41-1. Bryozoan. 2. Sponge. 3. Crinoid. 4. Gastropod.

SOME TYPICAL FOSSILS

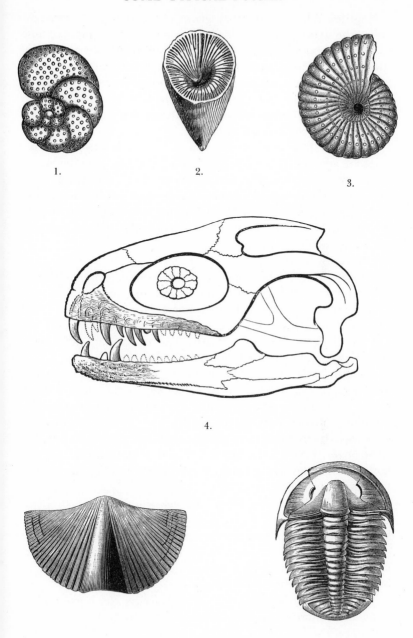

Fig. 42-1. Foraminifer. 2. Coral. 3. Ammonite. 4. Dinosaur skull.
5. Brachiopod. 6. Trilobite.

Reptiles. When the reptilian giants of the Mesozoic became extinct, the types that remained were nearly the same as those groups that exist today. However, huge land turtles were common, and alligators were much more abundant than they are now.

Birds. Toothless birds resembling modern forms appeared in the Eocene epoch. Among the now extinct birds were *Diatryma, Phororhacos, Dinornis* (which was 10 feet tall), and *Aepyornis* (which laid an egg over a foot long).

Mammals. Mammals occupy almost every habitat; their structures are adapted to burrow, climb, brachiate (swing by the arms), run, swim, and fly. The diverse forms that exist today have evolved from primitive mammals characterized by small size, short legs, flat, five-toed feet, small brains, long faces, and 44 low-crowned teeth. Evolutionary development and specialization have taken four principal directions:

1. Increase in size.

2. Increase in relative brain capacity, especially in the size of the cerebrum, which is the center of memory and intellect.

3. Specialization of teeth according to feeding habits; differentiation between carnivores, herbivores, and omnivores.

4. Specialization of the feet according to habitat; differentiation between animals that run, climb, dig, etc.

ARCHAIC MAMMALS. At the beginning of the Cenozoic era the dominant mammals were those belonging to four now extinct orders referred to as the "archaic mammals." These were the *creodonts,* predecessors of the catlike and wolflike carnivores; *amblypods,* a dominant group of ungulates (hoofed animals); *condylarths,* herbivorous ungulates; and *uintatheres,* giant, six-horned ungulates which flourished in North America during the latter part of the Eocene.

Four other Paleocene orders, the *marsupials, insectivores, rodents,* and *primates* were associated with the archaic mammals, but persisted after the archaic mammals became extinct.

In the Eocene epoch most of the present-day orders of mammals were represented by ancestral stocks in North America. A brief summary of these types follows.

THE HORSE. Originating in North America, the horse underwent an evolution that has been extraordinarily well recorded. *Eohippus,* the "dawn horse," was a slender animal about a foot high, with four functional toes on the front foot and three on the hind foot. In an almost straight line of evolution, there followed *Mesohippus* of the Oligocene, *Merychippus* of the Miocene, *Pliohippus* of the Pliocene, and finally *Equus,* the wild horse of Pliocene and Pleistocene times; during this development the horse grew in size, lost the use of all but one toe (which enlarged to become the hoof), and developed long jaws and high-crowned teeth suitable for grazing. Horses died out in the New World until the Spaniards brought them in again.

THE RHINOCEROS. Like the horse, the rhinoceros originated in North America and then disappeared from this continent. It was extremely numerous during the Tertiary. The evolution of the rhinoceros is much more complex than that of the horse; in the Tertiary there were several families—a group that ran, an amphibious group that lived like the hippopotamus, and the "true rhinoceroses" which were the antecedents of the modern species. An Asiatic species of the early Tertiary was *Baluchitherium,* a true rhinoceros that stood 13 feet high at the shoulder, with a length of perhaps 25 feet—the most ponderous of all land animals.

THE TITANOTHERE. Another huge animal, distantly related to both horse and rhinoceros, was the titanothere. In the final stage of its evolution it attained elephantine size; it had a pair of long, bony horns on the skull. A poor brain and degenerate teeth probably brought about its extinction.

THE CAMEL. Another mammal of North American extraction is the camel. It evolved along lines similar to those of the horse, and likewise became extinct on this continent.

THE OREODONT. Very numerous in North America but known nowhere else, the oreodont was a small grazing animal which flourished on the western prairies. It was almost the size of a sheep and is thought to be an ancestor of the camel.

THE PROBOSCIDEANS. The amazing animals that possess a "trunk" originated in Egypt and expanded over the world in several groups. The *mastodon* (distinguished by its conical teeth) and the *true elephant* (with laminated teeth) are two well-known proboscideans. The *imperial mammoth* and the *woolly mammoth* are vanished Pleistocene members of the true elephant line.

CARNIVORES. From the creodonts of the Eocene, carnivores descended in two lines of evolution: one line comprised the civets, the hyenas, and the cats; the other line included the weasels, the raccoons, the bears, and the dogs. During the Pleistocene there existed a family of cats whose highly developed canines were adapted for stabbing and slicing rather than biting. These cats, of which *Smilodon* (saber-toothed cat or tiger) is an example, became extinct at the end of the Pleistocene, and the true "biting" cats went on to achieve their present distribution.

PRIMATES. Although the oldest known primate has been found in Paleocene deposits in Wyoming, the later primates evolved in the Old World. This order includes the lemurs, tarsiers, monkeys, and apes. Man is also a primate, sharing with the others his elongated limbs, enlarged hands and feet equipped with nails, apposable thumb (as well as first toe) for grasping and manipulation, and stereoscopic color vision. Together with the other anthropoids (monkeys and apes), man has a large brain, forward-facing eyes, and more specialized teeth.

Progress of Man. Tracing the course of man's evolution is beset with difficulties, and only the most general statements can be made with any degree of confidence. As a primate, man branched from the family tree near the end of the Pliocene epoch and he is distinguished by erect posture and rapidly increasing development of brain capacity, speech, and thought. The Pleistocene epoch saw the dramatic rise of manlike beings, whose evolution may have been stimulated by the challenge of changing climates. "Early man" became a cunning hunter, using weapons of stone, wood, bone, and shell, and subsisting on game, fruits, nuts, and herbs.

The oldest evidently human remains are those found since 1959 in East Africa (Olduvai Gorge, Tanganyika); called *Zinjanthropus,* he dates to about 1,500,000 years ago (Lower Pleistocene) and is regarded as a subgenus of *Australopithecus,* which also included *Paranthropus* of South Africa. Perhaps the next oldest human fossils belong to *Pithecanthropus,* which includes such familiar fossils as *Java man* (from Java), *Heidelberg man* (from Germany), and *Sinanthropus* (*Peking man,* from China). These may be close ancestors of the famous *Neanderthal man,* also discovered in Germany. From Upper Pleistocene rocks there, the first complete human skeletons were assembled, but Neanderthal man has since been found in places as widespread as northern Africa and western Asia.

The first true man of our species, *Homo sapiens,* appeared about 35,000 years ago and left many remains in Upper Pleistocene strata. Known as *Cro-Magnon* man, he was tall and had a large brain capacity. His implements of flint and bone are well made, and his highly developed artistic ability is shown by his cave paintings.

Man arrived in the New World during the Pleistocene (doubtless across a Bering land bridge between Siberia and Alaska), thereafter penetrating all North and South America. Much has been learned in recent years about the American Indian and his antecedents, and the radiocarbon method of age determination has been of considerable help in dating human relics, but this story belongs to archaeology and anthropology rather than to geology.

REVIEW QUESTIONS

1. Outline the subdivisions of the Cenozoic era.
2. Give the history of the Atlantic and Gulf coastal plains.
3. What are the main Cenozoic features in the Appalachian Mountains?
4. What are the main Cenozoic features in the Rocky Mountains?
5. Locate the Colorado Plateau, Basin and Range province, and Columbia Plateau.
6. Why is the Cenozoic history of the Pacific coast so complex?
7. What happened in western North America during the Cascadian revolution?
8. What great European mountains were created during the Cenozoic era?
9. Name the most valuable mineral resources of the Cenozoic age.
10. State four lines of evidence for repeated glaciations during the Pleistocene epoch?
11. Outline the subdivisions of the Pleistocene epoch, including both glacial and interglacial ages.
12. What regions of the world were glaciated during the Pleistocene epoch?

13. Name five important effects of the glaciation.
14. Summarize the evolution of the horse.
15. Name some of the human ancestors of present-day man.

SAMPLE FINAL EXAMINATION

The questions asked at the end of the individual chapters in this book are mostly of the esssay type, requiring an organized discussion answer; therefore, they are best handled by taking time to plan the answer and stating it as clearly as possible.

The following examination is designed to furnish examples of most of the various kinds of "objective" questions commonly asked in final examinations. They cover a wider range of information than the essay questions, they are much quicker to grade, and the results do not differ according to the interpretation of the person correcting them; hence they are often used for large classes. An understanding of technical vocabulary is the key to answering objective examination questions.

Lists and Classifications:

1. Prepare a short, tabular outline of igneous rocks, based on texture and mineral content.
2. Outline a classification of sedimentary rocks, distinguishing between clastic and nonclastic.
3. Outline a classification of metamorphic rocks.
4. List the phyla of the animal kingdom, indicating those most important as fossils.
5. Outline the geologic time chart.
6. Outline a classification of the dinosaurs.

Definition. Identify the technical terms referred to in the following definitions:

1. Sediment deposited by streams (general term).
2. Wind-blown glacial silt and clay, forming bluffs.
3. Arid-land equivalent of a peneplain.
4. Erosion remnant on a peneplain.
5. Equivalence of strata from one place to another.
6. Granular ice derived from fallen snow.
7. Middle strata in a delta.
8. Lowest altitude to which a given stream can erode its channel at a given time.
9. Stone beveled by wind abrasion (general term).
10. Arid-climate terrain in closely dissected soft rocks.
11. Kind of stream flowing over coastal plain or other original slope.

237

12. Topography containing many sinks.
13. Succession of ocean waves set in movement by submarine earthquake.
14. Stream pattern on homogenous rocks.
15. Boundary between vadose zone and zone of saturation.
16. Glacial boulder resting on foreign rock.
17. Igneous rock consisting of very large grains.
18. Circular coral reef surrounding a lagoon.
19. Break in sequence of sedimentation.
20. Principle of the continuity of geologic processes.

Arrangement in Sequence:

1. Name the following categories of classification in order from most general to most specialized: families, species, classes, orders, phyla, genera.
2. Give the chronological order of the following orogenies: Nevadian disturbance, Acadian disturbance, Grand Canyon disturbance, Laramide revolution, Cascadian revolution, Laurentian disturbance.
3. Name in sequence the glacial and interglacial ages of the Pleistocene epoch.

Multiple Choice:

1. Which one of the following is a second-order relief feature: Greenland, Mount Shasta, Pacific Ocean Basin, Great Plains, Lake Como?
2. Which one of the following topographic features can be formed by either erosion or deposition: roche moutonnée, stream terrace, hook, stalactite, loess?
3. Which one of the following places is most noted for its thermal activity: Iceland, Egypt, Cuba, Korea, Ecuador?
4. Which one of the following is a third-order relief feature: Colorado Plateau, Africa, Nile Delta, Alps, Indian Ocean Basin?
5. Which one of the following kinds of animal life was *not* dominant during the Paleozoic era: marine invertebrates, fishes, trilobites, corals, mammals?
6. Which one of the following kinds of animals is extinct: *Homo sapiens,* titanothere, foraminifer, coral, primate?
7. Which one of the following was a Pleistocene predecessor of the Great Lakes: Ontario, Lahontan, Agassiz, Algonquin, Bonneville?
8. Which one of the following rocks is geologically unlike the others: granite, andesite, limestone, basalt, gabbro?
9. Which one of the following minerals makes ground water hard: feldspar, calcite, quartz, hematite, hornblende?

Matching. Indicate by the correct letter which of the following agents of erosion and deposition is responsible for each of the geologic features listed below.

a. Stream   *b.* Ground water   *c.* Glacier   *d.* Ocean   *e.* Wind

1. Spit	6. Floodplain
2. Kame	7. Hook
3. Pot hole	8. Till
4. Dreikanter	9. Wind gap
5. Bergschrund	10. Stalactite

Indicate by the correct letter which of the following classes of geologic materials each of the minerals and rocks listed below belongs in.

a. Mineral   *b.* Intrusive igneous rock   *c.* Extrusive igneous rock
d. Sedimentary rock   *e.* Metamorphic rock

1. Gneiss	11. Slate
2. Quartz	12. Shale
3. Obsidian	13. Biotite
4. Coal	14. Sandstone
5. Gabbro	15. Felsite
6. Hematite	16. Pyrite
7. Basalt	17. Syenite
8. Feldspar	18. Quartzite
9. Schist	19. Halite
10. Conglomerate	20. Granite

Selection. Indicate whether the following geologic features are erosional (E) or depositional (D).

1. Pediment	9. Esker
2. Fiord	10. Cirque
3. Concretion	11. Tombolo
4. Col	12. Tarn
5. Drumlin	13. Stalagmite
6. Spouting horn	14. Barchan
7. Bajada	15. Sea stack
8. Varve	

ANSWERS TO SAMPLE FINAL EXAMINATION

Lists and Classifications:
1. See Table 2 (p. 81).
2. See Table 3 (p. 86).
3. See Table 4 (p. 93).
4. See pages 180–181.
5. See Table 5 (p. 191).
6. See pages 217–218.

Definition: 1. alluvium. 2. loess. 3. pediment. 4. monadnock. 5. correlation. 6. névé or firn. 7. foreset beds. 8. base level. 9. ventifact. 10. badlands. 11. consequent stream. 12. karst. 13. tsunamis. 14. dendritic. 15. water table. 16. erratic. 17. pegmatite. 18. atoll. 19. unconformity. 20. uniformitarianism.

Arrangement in Sequence:

1. Phyla, classes, orders, families, genera, species.
2. Laurentian disturbance, Grand Canyon disturbance, Acadian disturbance, Nevadian disturbance, Laramide revolution, Cascadian revolution.
3. See page 226.

Multiple Choice: 1. Great Plains. 2. Stream terrace. 3. Iceland. 4. Nile Delta. 5. Mammals. 6. Titanothere. 7. Algonquin. 8. Limestone. 9. Calcite.

Matching: 1. *d.* 2. *a.* 3. *c.* 4. *d.* 5. *b.* 6. *a.* 7. *c.* 8. *a.* 9. *e.* 10. *d.* 11. *e.* 12. *d.* 13. *a.* 14. *d.* 15. *c.* 16. *a.* 17. *b.* 18. *e.* 19. *a.* 20. *b.*

Selection: 1. E. 2. E. 3. D. 4. E. 5. D. 6. E. 7. D. 8. D. 9. D. 10. E. 11. D. 12. E. 13. D. 14. D. 15. E.

Selected Bibliography

REFERENCE BOOKS

General References:

Glossary of Geology and Related Sciences. Washington, D.C., American Geological Institute, 1960. Abridgment: *Dictionary of Geological Terms.* New York, Doubleday, 1962.

Pangborn, Mark W., Jr. *Earth for the Layman,* Washington, D.C., American Geological Institute, 1957.

Pearl, Richard M. *Guide to Geologic Literature.* New York, McGraw-Hill, 1951.

Field and Mining Geology:

Compton, Robert R. *Manual of Field Geology.* New York, Wiley, 1962.

Forrester, James Donald. *Principles of Field and Mining Geology.* New York, Wiley, 1946.

Lahee, Frederic H. *Field Geology,* 6th ed. New York, McGraw-Hill, 1961.

LeRoy, L. W. *Subsurface Geologic Methods,* 2nd ed. Golden, Colorado School of Mines, 1951.

Low, Julian W. *Geologic Field Methods.* New York, Harper, 1957.

McKinstry, Hugh E. *Mining Geology* Englewood Cliffs, N.J., Prentice-Hall, 1948.

Shrock, Robert R. *Sequence in Layered Rocks; A Study of Features and Structures.* New York, McGraw-Hill, 1948.

Mineralogy:

Dana, Edward Salisbury, and Ford, William E. *A Textbook of Mineralogy, With an Extended Treatise on Crystallography and Physical Mineralogy,* 4th ed. New York, Wiley, 1932.

Palache, Charles; Berman, Harry; and Frondel, Clifford. *The System of Mineralogy of James Dwight Dana and Edward Salsibury Dana,* 7th ed. New York, Wiley, Vol. I, 1944; Vol. 2, 1951; Vol. 3, 1962.

Paleontology:

Arnold, Chester A. *An Introduction to Paleobotany.* New York, McGraw-Hill, 1947.

Beerbower, James R. *Search for the Past; An Introduction to Paleontology.* Englewood Cliffs, N.J., Prentice-Hall, 1960.

Darrah, William C. *Principles of Paleobotany,* 2nd ed. New York, Ronald, 1960.

Easton, William H. *Invertebrate Paleontology.* New York, Harper, 1960.

Moore, Raymond C.; Lalicker, Cecil G.; and Fischer, Alfred G. *Inverte-brate Fossils*. New York, McGraw-Hill, 1952.

Romer, Alfred Sherwood, *Vertebrate Paleontology*. Chicago, University of Chicago, 1945.

Shimer, Hervey W., and Shrock, Robert R. *Index Fossils of North America*. New York, Wiley, 1944.

Shrock, Robert R., and Twenhofel, William H. *Principles of Inverte-brate Paleontology*. New York, McGraw-Hill, 1953.

HISTORY OF GEOLOGY

Adams, Frank Dawson. *The Birth and Development of the Geological Sciences*. New York, Dover, 1954.

Fenton, Carroll Lane, and Fenton, Mildred Adams. *Giants of Geology*. New York, Doubleday, 1952.

Geike, Sir Archibald. *The Founders of Geology*. New York, Macmillan, 1905.

Merrill, George P. *The First One Hundred Years of American Geology*. New Haven, Yale University, 1924.

INTERIOR OF THE EARTH

Bucher, Walter H. *The Deformation of the Earth's Crust; An Inductive Approach to the Problems of Diastrophism*. New York, Hafner, 1957.

Daly, Reginald Aldworth. *Architecture of the Earth*. New York, Apple-ton-Century-Crofts, 1938.

———. *Igneous Rocks and the Depths of the Earth*. New York, McGraw-Hill, 1933.

———. *Our Mobile Earth*. New York, Scribner's, 1926.

———. *Strength and Structure of the Earth*. Englewood Cliffs, N.J., Prentice-Hall, 1940.

Howell, Benjamin F., Jr. *Introduction to Geophysics*. New York, McGraw-Hill, 1959.

Jacobs, J. A.; Russell, R. D.; and Wilson, J. Tuzo. *Physics and Geology*. New York, McGraw-Hill, 1959.

VOLCANISM

Bullard, Fred M. *Volcanoes. In History, In Theory, In Eruption*. Austin, University of Texas, 1962.

Coleman, Satis N. *Volcanoes, New and Old*. New York, John Day, 1946.

Cotton, C. A. *Volcanoes as Landscape Forms*. New York, Wiley, 1953.

Rittmann, A. *Volcanoes and Their Activity*. Translated by E. A. Vin-cent. New York, Interscience (Wiley), 1962.

STRUCTURAL GEOLOGY

Billings, Marland P. *Structural Geology,* 2nd ed. Englewood Cliffs, N.J., Prentice-Hall, 1954.

de Sitter, L. U. *Structural Geology.* New York, McGraw-Hill, 1956.

Hills, E. Sherbon. *Outlines of Structural Geology.* 3rd ed. New York, Wiley, 1953.

Nevin, Charles Merrick. *Principles of Structural Geology,* 4th ed. New York, Wiley, 1949.

EARTHQUAKES

Byerly, Perry. *Seismology.* Englewood Cliffs, N.J., Prentice-Hall, 1942.

Eiby, G. A. *About Earthquakes.* New York, Harper, 1957.

Heck, Nicholas H. *Earthquakes.* Princeton, Princeton University, 1936.

Leet, L. D. *Practical Seismology and Seismic Prospecting.* New York, Appleton-Century-Crofts, 1938.

Lynch, Joseph. *Our Trembling Earth.* New York, Dodd, Mead, 1940.

Macelwane, James B. *When the Earth Quakes.* Milwaukee, Bruce, 1947.

Richter, Charles F. *Elementary Seismology.* San Francisco, Freeman, 1958.

ROCKS AND MINERALS

Industrial Minerals and Rocks (Nonmetallics other than Fuels), 3rd ed. New York, American Institute of Mining, Metallurgical, and Petroleum Engineers, 1960.

Bateman, Alan M. *Economic Mineral Deposits,* 2nd ed., New York, Wiley, 1950.

Bates, Robert L. *Geology of the Industrial Rocks and Minerals.* New York, Harper, 1960.

Berry, Leonard, and Mason, Brian. *Mineralogy.* San Francisco, Freeman, 1959.

Dennen, William. *Principles of Mineralogy.* New York, Ronald, 1959.

Dunbar, Carl O., and Rodgers, John. *Principles of Stratigraphy.* New York, Wiley, 1957.

Emmons, William Harvey. *The Principles of Economic Geology.* New York, McGraw-Hill, 1940.

George, Russell D. *Minerals and Rocks.* New York, Appleton-Century-Crofts, 1943.

Huang, Walter T. *Petrology.* New York, McGraw-Hill, 1962.

Kemp, James Furman, and Grout, Frank F. *A Handbook of Rocks, For Use Without the Petrographic Microscope,* 6th ed. Princeton, N.J., Van Nostrand, 1940.

Kraus, Edward Henry; Hunt, Walter Fred; and Ramsdell, Lewis Stephen. *Mineralogy; An Introduction to the Study of Minerals and Crystals,* 5th ed. New York, McGraw-Hill, 1959.

Krumbein, W. C., and Sloss, L. L., *Stratigraphy and Sedimentation.* New York, Wiley, 1957.

Ladoo, Raymond B., and Myers, W. M. *Nonmetallic Minerals,* 2nd ed. New York, McGraw-Hill, 1951.

Lilley, Ernest R. *Economic Geology of Mineral Deposits.* New York, Henry Holt, 1936.

Lindgren, Waldemar. *Mineral Deposits,* 4th ed. New York, McGraw-Hill, 1933.

Lovering, T. H. *Minerals in World Affairs.* Englewood Cliffs, N.J., Prentice-Hall, 1943.

Pearl, Richard M. *Rocks and Minerals.* New York, Barnes & Noble, 1956.

Pettijohn, F. J. *Sedimentary Rocks,* 2nd ed. New York, Harper, 1957.

Pirsson, Louis V., and Knopf, Adolph. *Rocks and Rock Minerals,* 3rd ed. New York, Wiley, 1947.

Ries, H. *Economic Geology.* New York, Wiley, 1937.

Riley, Charles M. *Our Mineral Resources.* New York, Wiley, 1959.

Rogers, Austin Flint. *Introduction to the Study of Minerals,* 3rd ed. New York, McGraw-Hill, 1937.

Shand, S. James. *Eruptive Rocks.* New York, Wiley, 1948.

Spock, L. E. *Guide to the Study of Rocks.* New York, Harper, 1953.

Voskuil. Walter H. *Minerals in World Industry.* New York, McGraw-Hill, 1955.

Wade, F. Alton, and Mattox, Richard B. *Elements of Crystallography and Mineralogy.* New York, Harper, 1960.

Weller, J. Marvin. *Stratigraphic Principles and Practice.* New York, Harper, 1960.

Winchell, Alexander N. *Elements of Mineralogy.* Englewood Cliffs, N.J., Prentice-Hall, 1942.

PROCESSES OF EROSION AND DEPOSITION

General Geomorphology:

Cotton, C. A. *Climatic Accidents in Landscape-Making.* New York, Wiley, 1948.

————. *Geomorphology; An Introduction to the Study of Landforms.* New York, Wiley, 1952.

————. *Landscape As Developed by the Processes of Normal Erosion,* 2nd ed. New York, Wiley, 1949.

Hinds, Norman E. A. *Geomorphology; The Evolution of Landscape.* Englewood Cliffs, N.J., Prentice-Hall, 1943.

Lobeck, A. K. *Geomorphology; An Introduction to the Study of Landscapes.* New York, McGraw-Hill, 1939.

Shuler, Ellis W. *Rocks and Rivers of America.* New York, Ronald, 1945.

Thornbury, William D. *Principles of Geomorphology.* New York, Wiley, 1954.

von Engeln, O. D. *Geomorphology; Systematic and Regional.* New York, Macmillan, 1942.

Worcester, Philip G. *A Textbook of Geomorphology,* 2nd ed. Princeton, N.J., Van Nostrand, 1948.

Regional Geomorphology:

Atwood, Wallace W. *The Physiographic Provinces of North America.* Boston, Ginn, 1940.

Fenneman, Nevin M. *Physiography of Eastern United States.* New York: McGraw-Hill, 1938.

————. *Physiography of Western United States.* New York, McGraw-Hill, 1931.

Loomis, Frederic B. *Physiography of the United States.* New York, Doubleday, 1937.

Shimer, John A. *This Sculptured Earth; The Landscape of America,* New York, Columbia University, 1959.

Special Geomorphology:

Bagnold, R. A. *The Physics of Blown Sand and Desert Dunes.* New York, Morrow, 1942.

Bauer, Leonard David. *Soil Physics,* 3rd ed. New York, Wiley, 1956.

Johnson, Douglas W. *Stream Sculptures on the Atlantic Slope.* New York, Columbia University, 1931.

Kuenen, P. H. *Realms of Water; Some Aspects of Its Cycle in Nature,* rev. ed. trans. by M. Hollander. New York, Wiley, 1955.

Meinzer, O. E. *Hydrology.* New York, McGraw-Hill, 1942.

Reiche, Parry. *A Survey of Weathering Processes and Products.* Albuquerque. University of New Mexico, 1950.

Sharpe, C. F. Stewart. *Landslides and Related Phenomena; A Study of Mass-Movements of Soil and Rock.* New York, Cooper Square, 1960.

Tolman, C. F. *Ground Water.* New York, McGraw-Hill, 1937.

MARINE GEOLOGY

Carson, Rachel L. *The Sea Around Us.* New York, Oxford University, 1951.

Daly, Reginald A. *The Floor of the Ocean; New Light on Old Mysteries.* Chapel Hill, University of North Carolina, 1942.

Johnson, Douglas Wilson, *Shore Processes and Shore Line Development.* New York, Wiley, 1919.

Kuenen, P. H. *Marine Geology.* New York, Wiley, 1950.

Pettersson, Hans. *The Ocean Floor.* New Haven, Yale University, 1954.

Shepard, Francis P. *Submarine Geology.* New York, Harper, 1948.

———. *The Earth Beneath the Sea.* Baltimore, John Hopkins, 1959.

MAPS

Dake, C. L. and Brown, J. S. *Interpretation of Topographic and Geologic Maps, With Special Reference to Determination of Structure.* New York, McGraw-Hill, 1925.

Greitzer, Samuel L. *Elementary Topography and Map Reading.* New York, McGraw-Hill, 1944.

Raisz, Erwin. *General Cartography,* 2nd ed. New York, McGraw-Hill, 1948.

———. *Principles of Cartography.* New York, McGraw-Hill, 1962.

Robinson, Arthur H. *Elements of Cartography,* 2nd ed. New York, Wiley, 1960.

ORIGIN OF THE EARTH AND SOLAR SYSTEM

Chamberlin, Thomas Chrowder. *The Two Solar Families; The Sun's Children.* Chicago, University of Chicago, 1930.

Gamow, George. *The Creation of the Universe.* New York, Viking, 1956.

Hoyle, Fred. *The Nature of the Universe,* 2nd ed. New York, Harper, 1960.

Jeans, Sir James. *The Universe Around Us,* 4th ed. New York, Macmillan, 1944.

Jeffreys, Harold. *The Earth,* 4th ed. New York, Cambridge University, 1959.

Russell, Henry Norris. *The Solar System and its Origin.* New York, Macmillan, 1935.

Singh, Jagjit. *Great Ideas and Theories of Modern Cosmology.* New York, Dover, 1961.

Smart, W. M. *The Origin of the Earth,* 2nd ed. Baltimore, Penguin, 1960.

Urey, Harold C. *The Planets, Their Origin and Development.* New Haven, Yale University, 1952.

FOSSILS AND EVOLUTION

Andrews, Henry N., Jr. *Ancient Plants, And the World They Live In.* Ithaca, N.Y., Comstock, 1947.

———. *Studies in Paleobotany.* New York, Wiley, 1961.

Colbert, Edwin H. *Dinosaurs, Their Discovery and Their World.* New York, Dutton, 1961.

———. *Evolution of the Vertebrates.* New York, Wiley, 1955.

Dodson, E. O. *Evolution: Process and Product.* New York, Reinhold, 1960.

Dobzhansky, Theodosius. *Mankind Evolving; The Evolution of the Human Species.* New Haven, Yale University, 1962.

Huxley, Julian S. *Evolution in Action.* New York, Harper, 1953.

Knowlton, Frank Hall. *Plants of the Past; A Popular Account of Fossil Plants.* Princeton, Princeton University, 1927.

LeGros Clark, W. E. *History of the Primates; An Introduction to the Study of Fossil Man.* Chicago, University of Chicago, 1957.

Merrell, David J. *Evolution and Genetics; The Modern Theory of Evolution.* New York, Holt, 1962.

Moody, Paul Amos. *Introduction to Evolution,* 2nd ed. New York, Harper, 1962.

Raymond, P. E. *Prehistoric Life.* Cambridge, Harvard University, 1939.

Rhodes, F. H. T. *The Evolution of Life.* Baltimore, Penguin, 1962.

Romer, Alfred Sherwood. *The Vertebrate Story.* Chicago, University of Chicago, 1959.

Ross, Herbert H. *A Synthesis of Evolutionary Theory.* Englewood Cliffs, N.J., Prentice-Hall, 1962.

Simpson, George G. *Life of the Past; An Introduction to Paleontology.* New Haven, Yale University, 1949.

———. *The Major Features of Evolution.* New York, Columbia University, 1953.

———. *The Meaning of Evolution; A Study of the History of Life and of Its Significance for Man.* New Haven, Yale University, 1960.

Stirton, R. A. *Time, Life, and Man: The Fossil Record.* New York, Wiley, 1959.

Tax, S., ed. *Evolution after Darwin,* 3 vols. Chicago, University of Chicago, 1960.

Weidenreich, Franz. *Apes, Giants, and Man.* Chicago, University of Chicago, 1946.

PLEISTOCENE GLACIATION

Coleman, A. P. *Ice Ages, Recent and Ancient.* New York, Macmillan, 1926.

————.*The Last Million Years; A History of the Pleistocene in North America.* Toronto, University of Toronto, 1941.

Daly, Reginald Aldworth. *The Changing World of the Ice Age.* New Haven, Yale University, 1934.

Dyson, James L. *The World of Ice.* New York, Knopf, 1962.

Flint, Richard Foster. *Glacial and Pleistocene Geology.* New York, Wiley, 1957.

Sharp, Robert P. *Glaciers.* Eugene, University of Oregon, 1960.

Index

69

21

$$\frac{5}{4} \qquad \frac{5}{3} \qquad \frac{5}{3} = 2$$

$$2x + 1 = 3x + 2$$

$$-1 = x$$

$$6\left(\frac{x}{2} + 1\right) = \left(\frac{x}{3} + 2\right)6$$

$$3x + 1 = 2x + 2$$

$$x = 1$$

$$\frac{x}{2} = -1 \qquad\qquad \frac{x}{2} + 1 = \frac{x}{3} + 2$$

$$x = -2 \qquad\qquad 3x + 1 = 2x + 2$$

$$-6 + 1 = -4 + 2$$

$$\frac{x}{2} + 1 = \frac{2}{3} + 2 \qquad -5 = -2$$

$$= 0 \quad 2$$